Speech Communication 212: Workbook

Spring 2012

Dr. Amy Slagell
Director of the Basic Course
Iowa State University

Speech Communication 212: Fundamentals of Public Speaking
Spring 2012

Dr. Crosby   Email: rbcrosby@iastate.edu
308B Carver Hall   Office hours: Tuesdays and Thursdays from 10-12 and by appointment

And so the teaching of communication will always be with us in some honored or fugitive place just as it has been with us for twenty centuries or more. It will be with us for the most fundamental of reasons: Freedom goes to the articulate. After all, with effective communication I decide who will pay me or love me or vote for me. With effective communication I decide if my people will continue to suffer social discrimination or joblessness or mental distress. With effective communication I decide who will share my truths, honor my gods, appreciate my history.

-Dr. Roderick Hart, University of Texas at Austin

Welcome to the Fundamentals of Public Speaking. In this course you will work to develop practical skills for success such as how to build speeches that people will want to hear and how to deliver them so they will want to hear more. You will also work to develop skills for life such as rhetorical sensitivity, critical thinking, and self-confidence. Like any class concerned with communication skills, you can expect to discover new things about yourself as well as others.

Required Texts & Resources:
1) Stephen E. Lucas, <u>The Art of Public Speaking</u>, 10th edition. McGraw-Hill, 2009 available at the book store OR you may purchase the eBook which comes with access to online learning materials. The ebook is available directly from the publisher by clicking on eBook in our Blackboard course website; ebook registration cards are also available in the ISU Bookstore.
2) Amy R. Slagell, Speech Communication 212, 16th Edition, Spring 2012 Workbook
3) Course Blackboard Site

Assignments:

Exams, Quizzes, and Classwork Assignments:
    3 Exams 20%
    5 Lecture Quizzes 10%
    Classwork 20%

Major Speaking Assignments:
    Informative Speech 15%
    Persuasive Speech 20%
    Special Occasion Speech 15%

How to Succeed:

Rule #1: Attend Class Well Prepared
By coming prepared to class regularly you will learn the expectations and criteria for each assignment as well as learning strategies that will help you succeed. We want you to develop confidence as a communicator; we want you to do well; we want you to be an audience for your classmates in an effort to become a more effective listener. You need to be in class for those things to happen and you need to do the readings and exercises on the syllabus for the sake of learning.

Attendance in Lecture and Lab will allow you to practice your listening and speaking skills. Excellent attendance will help you succeed. First, you will get the information you need, and second, you will earn bonus classwork points. All quizzes will be given in Lecture and daily attendance taken in Lab. Zero Lab absences earns a 10-point bonus; one absence a 6-point bonus, and 2 misses a 3-point bonus. Because these are points *for* attendance, they cannot be "made up" by anything other than <u>attendance</u>, even if the absence is excused.

Poor attendance will hurt your potential for success and is unfair to classmates who need an audience. For every recorded Lab absence beyond 4 you will lose 10 points per day in addition to whatever points you missed the opportunity to earn during that class session. **Students who accumulate 7 or more Lab absences (regardless of the cause) will not be able to pass the class.**

Rule # 2: Do Assignments on Time

The speaking assignments are carefully scheduled to give everyone an equal amount of speaking time during the semester. The exercises and Blackboard assignments all aim to help you develop the skills you need to complete major assignments successfully. Keep up with your daily work and reading and you can easily do well.

Speeches must be delivered on the day assigned. Failure to show up or contact your lab instructor on your speaking day will result in an "F" on the speech. Should extraordinary circumstances arise and you decide you cannot speak on the day assigned, you must be in contact with your Lab instructor before class to discuss arrangements and their consequences (penalty is typically a full letter grade deduction for each class period the speech is late). Should a scheduling conflict arise, you can arrange to give a speech early without penalty.

All 3 major speeches (Informative, Persuasive, and Special Occasion) must be delivered in order to pass the course.

Turn in your written assignments either through Blackboard or to your instructor as directed. Unexcused late work will not earn full classwork points, but you must still turn in assignments like speech topic forms in order to get feedback from your instructor. If you know ahead of time that you will be gone you must make arrangements to turn in your work early.

Outlines for the informative and persuasive speeches and the manuscripts for the special occasion speech are to be typed and carefully proofread. Draft outlines are due on workshop days. Final outlines are due at the beginning of class on the day your speech is due and must be uploaded into Blackboard by the end of that day.

Rule # 3: Use the Resources Available to Help You

- Use the 212 Workbook, Textbook, and Blackboard site regularly.
- Go to the library; use the Expanded Academic Index and the Class Guides provided online.
- Ask questions; rely on your Lab instructor, classmates, and Lecturer instructor to help.
- Maximize your classwork points; plan ahead and earn make-up points to learn more and to recover lost points.
- If you need accommodations to help you succeed in this class talk to Dr. Crosby during office hours and be sure to visit the Disabilities Resources Office, room 1076 Student Services Building (phone: 294-6624).

Rule # 4: Stay Honest

In this class we value your own voice, experiences and efforts. You can only learn by writing, developing and practicing your own speeches. If you do not understand plagiarism, please read Ch. 2 in the Textbook. Students suspected of Academic Dishonesty or Plagiarism will need to meet with their instructor and the course lecturer to explore the facts and discuss the penalties and the process. Disputed and clear cases will be turned over to the Dean of Students. See W (Workbook) pp. 12-13, 29-32, 62-64, Chapters 2 and 6 of the Textbook, the Blackboard site and sample speeches for information about research and citing sources both orally and in written forms so you can avoid these charges. If you are struggling in any way to get your work completed because of time or other constraints, talk to your lab instructor or lecturer before the assignment is due.

January/February 2012

Sun	Mon	Tue	Wed	Thu	Fri	Sat
8	9 LECTURE What is this course about, how does it work, and how can you do well?	10	11 LECTURE What makes a good public speaker? Workbook (W): Read pp. 8-13 Textbook (T): Read ch. 1 and do #2 Exercises for Critical Thinking, Blackboard : Visit the site and enroll in Blackboard.	12	13 LAB Meet your lab classmates. Discuss Ethics and Intro Speech. W: Bring W to class T: Read ch. 2 Blackboard: Background survey due by midnight	14
15	16 No Class University Holiday	17	18 LAB Deliver Introductory Speeches W: Do assignment p. 16	19	20 LAB Finish Introductory Speeches Form Learning Groups and Introduce Paired Perspectives W: Read pp. 20-27 **T: Read ch. 4, do #4 Exercises for Critical Thinking**	21
22	23 LECTURE Informative Speaking **1st QUIZ** W: Read pp. 28-32; 35-37 T: Read chs. 8 & 1st half of 14	24	25 LECTURE How do you begin and end? How do you move from point to point? T: Read ch. 9 W: Do Flawed Introductions Exercise, p. 45	26	27 LAB How do you build an outline? Paired Perspectives Prep. T: Read ch. 10 W: Do p. 44 **Blackboard: Sign up for Speaking Days for the Semester**	28
29	30 LAB Deliver Paired Perspectives Speeches T: Read Ch. 3, esp. Section "Giving your first speech" W: Bring p. 113 to class	31	**February 1 LAB** Deliver Paired Perspectives Speeches Discuss Informative Speech Topics W: Bring p. 113 to class **Blackboard: Informative Speech Topic Form Due by Midnight**	2	3 LECTURE How do you keep from being boring? Develop your ideas! W: Read pp. 14-15; 41-43 T: Read 2nd half of ch. 14 (including the speech) & 1st half of ch. 5 (stop at Demographic Analysis)	4
5	6 LECTURE How do you keep from being boring? Use strong delivery and visual aids! T: Read chs. 12 & 13 W: Read pp. 46-50	7	8 LECTURE EXAM I (chs. 1, 2, 4, 8, 9, 10, 12, 13 & 14)	9	10 LAB Delivery Exercises W: Read p. 53 & work on your speech	11
12	13 LAB Informative Speech Workshop 1 Speakers for the first 2 days of persuasive speeches come to Lab with 2 copies of completed outlines for workshop activities. (follow example on W pp. 35-37)	14	15 LAB Deliver Informative Speeches Speakers: Bring a copy of final outline and W p. 115 – upload outline to Blackboard. Critics: Bring peer critique forms, W pp. 117, 119.	16	17 LAB Deliver Informative Speeches Speakers: Bring a copy of final outline and W p. 115 – upload outline to Blackboard. Critics: Bring peer critique forms, W pp. 117, 119	18

February/March 2012

Sun	Mon	Tue	Wed	Thu	Fri	Sat
19	**20 LAB** Informative Speech Workshop 2 Speakers for last 3 days bring 2 copies of your preparation outline for the Informative Speech (follow example on W pp. 35-37)	21	**22 LAB** Deliver Informative Speeches Speakers: Bring a copy of final outline and W p. 115 – upload outline to Blackboard. Critics: Bring peer critique forms, W pp. 117, 119.	23	**24 LAB** Deliver Informative Speech Speakers: Bring a copy of final outline and W p. 115 – upload outline to Blackboard. Critics: Bring peer critique forms, W pp. 117, 119.	25
26	27 LECTURE Persuasive Speaking: What is it and what do you need to do to get started? T: Read 1st half of ch. 15; do # 2, Exercises for Critical Thinking W: Read pp. 56-61	28	29 LECTURE How do you organize ideas to help make them work? T: Read 2nd half of ch. 15; do #4, Exercises for Critical Thinking W: Read pp. 65-74	1	**March 2 LECTURE** How do you prove it? Use Support Materials and Reasoning! **QUIZ** T: Read ch. 16; do # 2, Exercises for Critical Thinking W: read pp. 62-64; 75-79	3
4	**5 LAB** Persuasive Speech Exercises 1 ***Bring questions about the speech assignment to class.*** W: Read p. 80 T: Read ch. 7; do # 1 & 2 in Exercises for Critical Thinking **Blackboard: Persuasive Speech Topic Ideas Analysis form due by midnight**	6	7 LECTURE How do you increase your persuasive power? Make the most of Language use, delivery and visual aids. W: Read pp. 82-83 T: Use ch. 6 as needed	8	**9 No Class** Enjoy your break!	10
18	**19 LAB** Persuasive Speech Exercises 2 **Blackboard: Researching the Persuasive Speech Worksheet due by midnight**	20	**21 LAB Workshop 1** Speakers for the first 3 days of persuasive speeches come to Lab with 2 copies of completed outlines for workshop activities. Look at examples in W pp. 70-79 for help.	22	23 LECTURE **EXAM 2 (chs. 6, 7, 15, 16)**	24
25	**26 LAB** Deliver Persuasive Speeches Speakers: Bring final outline and W p. 121 – upload your outline to Blackboard. Critics: Bring peer critique forms, W pp. 123, 125.	27	**28 LAB** Deliver Persuasive Speeches Speakers: Bring final outline and W p. 121 – upload your outline to Blackboard. Critics: Bring peer critique forms, W pp. **123, 125.**	29	**30 No class**	31

April 2012

Sun	Mon	Tue	Wed	Thu	Fri	Sat
1	**2 LAB Workshop 2** Speakers for the last 2 days of persuasive speeches come to Lab <u>with 2 copies of completed outlines</u> for workshop activities. Look at examples in W pp. 70-79 for help.	3	**4 LAB** <u>Deliver Persuasive Speeches</u> Speakers: <u>Bring final outline</u> and <u>W p. 121 – upload your outline to Blackboard.</u> Critics: Bring peer critique forms, <u>W pp. 123, 125.</u>	5	**6 LAB** <u>Deliver Persuasive Speeches</u> (Intro to Special Occasion) Speakers: <u>Bring final outline and W p. 121 – upload your outline to Blackboard.</u> Critics: Bring peer critique forms, <u>W pp. 123, 125.</u>	7
8	**9 LAB** <u>Deliver Persuasive Speeches</u> Speakers: <u>Bring final outline and W p. 121 – upload your outline to Blackboard.</u> Critics: Bring peer critique forms, <u>W pp. 123, 125.</u> W: Read pp. 88-92	10	**11 Lecture** Speaking on Special Occasions & Language Use T: Read "Commemorative Speeches in Ch. 17 W: Read pp. 93-104	12	**13 LECTURE** Special Occasion Speeches and Course Summation **Final Quiz** & read Ch. 11, do #3 in Exercises for Critical Thinking **Blackboard: Special Occasion Topic form due at Midnight**	14
15	**16 Lab** Stylistic Device Workshop **W: Do "Stylistic Devices Exercise," pp. 105-107**	17	**18 LAB** Special Occasion Speeches Workshop **Bring 2 copies of special occasion manuscript;** W: read pp. 108-109	19	**20 LAB** <u>IMPROMPTU SPEECHES</u> <u>W; p. 137</u>	21
22	**23 LAB** <u>Deliver Special Occasion Speeches</u> Speakers: Bring <u>final manuscript and W pp. 127, 129 – upload manuscript to Blackboard.</u> Critics: Bring <u>W, pp. 131, 133</u>	24	**25 LAB** <u>Deliver Special Occasion Speeches</u> Speakers: Bring <u>final manuscript and W pp. 127, 129 – upload manuscript to Blackboard.</u> Critics: Bring <u>W, pp 131, 133</u>	26	**27 LAB** <u>Deliver Special Occasion Speeches</u> Speakers: Bring <u>final manuscript and W pp. 127, 129 – upload manuscript to Blackboard.</u> Critics: Bring <u>W, pp 131, 133</u> **Final Day for Any Assignment Submission**	28

212A, 2 p.m. Lecture <u>FINAL EXAM:</u> Wed. May 2nd from 2:15-4:15 in LECTURE HALL

212B, 3 p.m. Lecture <u>FINAL EXAM:</u> Thurs. May 3rd from 2:15-4:15 in LECTURE HALL

<u>Classwork assignments listed by the order in which they are due:</u>

Background Survey	___ out of 5
Introductory Speech	___ out of 10
Paired Perspective Speech Topic Form	___ out of 10
Paired Perspective Speech	___ out of 15
Informative Speech Topic Form	___ out of 10
Informative Speech Workshop	_._ out of 10
Informative Speech Final Outline	___ out of 20
2 Informative Speech Peer Critiques	___ out of 10
Persuasive Speech Topic Form	___ out of 15
Researching the Persuasive Speech	___ out of 15
Persuasive Speech Workshop	___ out of 10
Persuasive Speech Final Outline	___ out of 20
2 Persuasive Speech Peer Critiques	___ out of 10
Special Occasion Speech Topic Form	___ out of 10
Impromptu Speech	___ out of 10
Outside Speech Observation Form*	___ out of 10
Special Occasion Speech Workshop	___ out of 10
Special Occasion Speech Final Manuscript	___ out of 10
2 Special Occasion Speech Peer Critiques	___ out of 10

<u>Total Possible Classwork Points</u>   ___ out of 220

<u>Make-Up Work Options to Replace Missed Classwork Points:</u>

I gave a Speech! Bonus Real Speech Reflection*	___ out of 5
Bonus Outside Speech Observation Form*	___ out of 5
Bonus Speech Recording Reflection*	___ out of 10
Attendance Bonus	___ out of 10
Lab Bonus	___ out of 10

*These assignments must be submitted within one week of when the speech was seen, recorded, or presented. The last day for any submission is April 27th.

SpCm 212 Final Grades are based on the following Weighted Totals: 3 Exams 20%, 5 Lecture Quizzes 10%, Classwork 20%, Informative Speech 15%, Persuasive Speech 20%, Special Occasion Speech 15%

A   93 - 100
A- 90 - 92.99
B+ 88 - 89.99
B   83 - 87.99
B- 80 - 82.99
C+ 78 – 79.99
C   73 – 77.99
C- 70 – 72.99
D+ 68 – 69.99
D   63 – 67.99
D- 60 – 62.99

Table of Contents

Unit III: *Speaking on Special Occasions*

Feedback Forms and Miscellaneous Materials

Key forms from Blackboard (in case your computer is down or you think better on paper; brainstorm here and then fill it out on Blackboard)

Introductory Materials

Welcome to Speech Communication 212:
Fundamentals of Public Speaking

SPCM 212 is a course that will challenge you on many different levels. Taught in the university setting, it is a skills course as well as a theory course. In lecture we will peruse the foundations of strong communication skills, ponder the nuts and bolts of building a good speech, and probe the mysteries of skillful delivery. In your lab sections you will have the opportunity to develop your speeches and display your speaking skills before a small, but appreciative, audience.

The Lecture/Lab format of the course requires that some days you attend the large group lecture and other days you attend your lab section. You will need to pay particular attention to the course syllabus. You will need to keep up with reading and homework assignments and mark your calendars to know when you are to attend lecture and when you are to attend lab. Lab days are in bold print on your syllabus. The course uses Blackboard where you will be automatically registered and where you will find a link to the required ebook for the course. You'll use these resources regularly.

Please bring the workbook with you to class regularly.

The SPCM 212 course objectives include:

- Developing rhetorical sensitivity. The course aims to develop your skills as an audience-centered communicator. The goal of the speeches we give in this course is to make a contribution to the knowledge or lives of our audience members. This goal will guide your choice of topic, material, structure and delivery style.

- Developing critical thinking skills. Your analysis of your audience, of the assignment, and of the topics of your speeches will lead to your careful selection and arrangement of material. Outlining your speeches forces clear and distinct development of ideas. Recognizing the relationship between claims and arguments will help make you a more persuasive arguer and a more critical listener.

- Developing competent delivery skills. Knowledge of the aspects of delivery, practice at delivery, and the observation of other speakers' delivery habits will help you make good choices about the delivery behaviors most appropriate for your audience and topic as well as for you. Recording your speeches and reviewing them will give you the chance to make great strides in this area.

- Developing a public communication ethic. When you speak you take on ethical responsibilities by engaging not only the time but also the minds of your audiences. Through the study of good speaking principles and the analysis of sample speeches, this course aims to develop your awareness of the ethical dimensions of public speaking so that you both uphold ethical standards in your own speeches and support principled communication choices in the speakers you choose to endorse.

Why Public Speaking?

Excerpts from Amy R. Slagell, "Public Speaking", in *21st Century Communication: A Reference Handbook*. Ed. by William F. Eadie, SAGE Publications, 2009, 194-201.

In everyday language "public speaking" refers to the communication practice of a speaker sharing ideas with an audience primarily through speech. The term encompasses a great many communication contexts including events as different as delivering an oral report on company profits to a closed meeting of a board of trustees, addressing millions of listeners around the globe during a U.S. presidential inauguration ceremony or giving a toast at a wedding. The fundamental notion underlying public speaking as a form of communication is that it is an embodied and oral act. Like written communication, public speaking is complicated because sharing meanings with others through language is difficult. The challenges of public speaking are heightened, however, since the speaker shares meaning not only through words but through body, voice and visuals. Furthermore, the public speaking experience, traditionally, is transitory; a speaker has one opportunity to accomplish her goal, to be understood by listeners. While readers can re-read documents until they understand the gist of the message, listeners, typically, cannot hear a speech again.

The presence of an audience is essential to the public speaking situation. Philosophers may debate the nature of "sound" when arguing about whether a tree falling in the forest makes a sound if no one is there to hear it, but theorists agree that the communicative act of public speaking requires the presence of a listener in order to be meaningful. Listeners bring their own experiences, languages, expectations and ways of making meaning into the public speaking interaction. The meanings taken away from a public speaking presentation depend upon the audience member's work in creating them. The more researchers investigate the ways people learn, the more it becomes clear that complex biological and social processes are at work as audience members construct their own meanings in communication contexts. Public Communication is a participatory process; a speaker cannot make himself understood without the willing participation of the listener in the process. The complexities of the mental landscapes of audience members—individually and as groups—is part of what makes public speaking a creative challenge that is never fully mastered.

Public Speaking in the 21st Century

It is perhaps surprising, in our increasingly mediated age, that the demand for public speakers persists. While information can be shared through many other means and persuasive appeals are pervasive on television, billboard and Internet, there remains a significant role for public speaking as a means for sharing ideas and motivating others. Political speaking is particularly visible in U.S. culture as we watch candidates participate in debates and see legislators and citizens speak about civic affairs on news shows, C-Span, community access television and Internet sites such as YouTube. Public speaking also happens at pep assemblies, in board rooms, during parent's night at public schools, in assembly halls and civic centers, at state fairs and trade shows, as part of award shows such as the Oscars, at commencements, at religious gatherings, inaugurations and weddings, in classrooms, prisons, legislatures, and even during meetings of 4-H or Rotary Clubs. Organizations such as the All American Speaker's Bureau will arrange for celebrities and professional speakers to address audiences at corporate meetings, trade shows, conventions and major community events. Though sometimes these appearances may include a chance to shake hands or get an autograph, their central purpose is to arrange to have someone with significant understanding of an issue, someone with a deep passion for a cause, someone with a fascinating experience to share, speak before an audience. Groups will pay speaking fees ranging from around $5,000, to hear, for example, Amy Henry from NBC's "The Apprentice," to over $200,000, to hear Donald Trump himself.

Contexts for and conceptualizations of public speaking have evolved over time. Today's speakers recognize that they do not simply transfer words and ideas to listeners, but rather are engaged in a complex process of attempting to share meanings among diverse members of an audience. This collaborative process means that public speakers must surrender the belief that they exercise entire control over the meanings constructed by audience members. The greatest challenge facing the contemporary public speaker is to adapt to the changing expectations and needs of their audiences. Emerging technologies are creating new opportunities for speakers to adapt to audiences, but they may also be changing the way audiences process information and create meanings.

Today's public speakers need to develop new strategies for gaining and maintaining audience attention. Integrating more visual elements and more audience interaction will help public speakers accomplish their goals. Instead of just talking about the structure of the pyramids of ancient Egypt, today's speakers can show audiences by using a series of images along with oral descriptions to offer something like a guided tour. In his lectures on global warming Al Gore doesn't use a long list of statistics to indicate the historical relationship between carbon in the atmosphere and temperature changes, instead he illustrates a suggestive relationship with animated lines that are drawn on a screen before the very eyes of his listeners. Anyone with an MP3 player and speakers can incorporate sound to help an audience of naturalists learn to distinguish between the calls of the barred owl and the great horned owl. Asking for a show of hands, using call and response strategies or having listeners participate in other ways will help speakers engage audiences increasing the likelihood that the message they are trying to share will be understood.

With so many avenues for gathering information and for communicating ideas open to the citizens of the 21st century, the central question for an aspiring speaker must be: what is the added value of using public speaking as the means of communication for a particular message? What is it that public speaking can offer that would be absent from a documentary, a narrated PowerPoint slide show, an email, blog or vlog posting? The answer, of course, is the presence of the speaker. There is high demand for the opportunity to experience firsthand the ideas, voice, facial expressions, gestures, energy, in a sense, the character of a speaker, through the public speaking context. The physical presence of a speaker conveys a level of attention of the speaker for that particular audience which is a gift every bit as desired as is the attention that audience is offering to the speaker. The possibility for an authentic connection between speakers and listeners continues and will continue to bring audiences together.

For Further Reading

Foss, S. & C. Griffin. (1995). Beyond persuasion: A proposal for an invitational rhetoric. *Communication Monographs*, 62, 2-18.

Lakoff, G. (2004). *Don't think of an elephant: know your values and frame the debate--The essential guide for progressives*. White River Junction, Vermont. Chelsea Green Publishing.

McCroskey. J.C. (2000). An introduction to rhetorical communication (8th ed.). Englewood Cliffs, NJ: Prentice Hall.

Richmond, V.P. & McCroskey, J.C. (1998). Communication: Apprehension, avoidance, and effectiveness (5th ed.). Needham Heights, MA: Allyn and Bacon.

Tufte, E.R. (2006). *Beautiful evidence*. Cheshire, CT: Graphics Press.

Brief Descriptions of Major Assignments

Speaking Assignments

Introductory Speech: A 2 minute prepared speech of introduction following one of the suggested topics. This speech offers a chance for an early assessment of your speaking skills. The goal is to give you a chance to speak in front of the class on the subject you know best with no formal grade pressure.

Paired Perspectives Speech: A 4 minute speech prepared and delivered with a partner that informs the audience about two different perspectives on a topic. The goal of the assignment is to practice the structural skills that lend clarity to oral communication. Your grade will be determined solely on how well you and your partner meet the formal requirements of speech structure and shared responsibility, so this is another chance to practice your delivery without grade pressure on that account. You'll create an outline together.

*Informative Speech: A 6 minute prepared speech to increase the audience's understanding of a process, concept, event, object, or person linked to your field of study or to the communication discipline. This is your first major speech. The goals are to prepare a clearly structured speech (so there is a full-sentence outline due for this speech), to use high quality information (so there are source requirements for this speech), and to communicate the subject to your audience clearly and memorably (so we expect rehearsal and lively delivery and audience engagement).

*Persuasive Speech of Policy: An 8 minute prepared speech aimed to persuade your audience to do something or to support an action to improve some aspect of life (like persuading them to donate blood, or persuading them that the university should adopt new green policies, or persuading them that the federal government should eliminate the penny). The goals are to prepare a clearly structured speech (so there is a formal outline due for this speech), to use high quality evidence (so there are source requirements for this speech), and to share interesting arguments and reasoning, tailored for this audience, delivered in a way that has an impact on your listeners (so we expect rehearsal and lively delivery and audience engagement).

*Special Occasion Speech: A 4.5 minute speech that aims either to inspire or to entertain the audience. It is your chance to develop your creative skills as a writer and speaker. The goals are to prepare a clear speech, using creative language (metaphor, repetition etc.) and to deliver it in such a way that it has an impact on the audience in terms of entertaining or inspiring them.

Impromptu Speeches: We'll do a few 1-2 minute unprepared speeches given from a simple topic assigned in class that day. This is your chance to prove that you can think on your feet and speak clearly (in both content and delivery).

Tests and Classwork

Exams: mostly multiple choice, some short answer

Classwork/Attendance: This includes points for your speech preparation and reflection work such as outlines, a manuscript, topic forms, peer critiques, quizzes, short speeches, workshops, and collected homework and in-class exercises. The attendance policy is clearly stated on the course syllabus.

* Failure to deliver any one of these major speeches will result in a grade of "F" for the course.

General Requirements for Speaking Assignments
That Can Have a Big Impact on Your Grade

1. **Delivering your speech on the day assigned.** No speeches can be delivered late without penalty. Be in touch with your instructor about emergencies. If you never get around to delivering one of the major speeches you will earn an "F" for the course.

2. **Avoiding Plagiarism and Academic Dishonesty.** Developing your ability to create the content of a speech is a goal of the course; shortcuts and cheating prevent you from achieving that goal. Students suspected of plagiarism or academic dishonesty will be called in to account for the work and the case will be turned over to the Dean of Students office for possible disciplinary action. Plagiarism and academic dishonesty charges and consequent grade penalties can also be made after you have completed the course.

Among the things you need to know in order to avoid plagiarism or academic dishonesty charges are the following:

a) <u>You may **not**</u>:
   - work with others to produce an individual speech for which more than one person tries to get credit.
   - present someone else's work as your own.
   - falsify supporting material/evidence or source citations.
   - lift ideas and wording from articles in printed sources or from the Internet without giving appropriate credit to them in writing and in oral citations. Do not simply cut and paste speech material or outline materials from the web.
   - string together quotes from others and call it your own outline or speech, even <u>with</u> citations.

b) <u>You may</u> (and are encouraged to):
   - seek out the advice of peers as you develop your speech.
   - share research resources with other students.
   - do research using quality resources and keep track of those sources.
   - visit with your TA during office hours to get help with the speech.
   - rehearse your speech with other students and revise in response to their critiques of your performance.
   -

Note: This is not a course in the oral interpretation of literature. It is a course that combines your inventive and presentational skills. Even with appropriate citation, if half of your speech is an extended quotation, you are not living up to the expectations of these assignments. Review class guidelines for use of and citation of sources in speeches and the material in chapter 2 of the text for further information about plagiarism.

3. **Time limits** will be strictly enforced for each assignment. Violations of the grace period will result in a third of a letter grade penalty for every 30 seconds or part thereof that you fall short of or go over time.

4. Complete, typed **full-sentence final outlines**, for the informative and persuasive speeches, and two complete, typed manuscripts for the special occasion speech, are due as assigned in class. Drafts of outlines/manuscripts should be completed by the workshop day indicated on the syllabus. Having no outline, a handwritten outline (without prior approval), or a clearly inadequate outline (half-page, blatantly incomplete) suggests you have not prepared for the assignment and you may not be permitted to speak. After your speeches, the outlines must be uploaded into the Blackboard site.

5. **Topics** for each assignment must be submitted to your lab instructor by the dates indicated on the syllabus. Be sure to check Blackboard to get your feedback!

Criteria Used for Evaluating Speeches

The following lists give you the general criteria by which you will be evaluated for each assignment. The grades you earn are based on your performance according to these criteria as well as your ability to meet the specific requirements of the assignment.

A *superior* **(A)** speech stands out from the crowd. It has superior content, excellent organization and distinctive delivery. In short, it represents the speaker's best creative effort. An **A** speech gets nearly everyone in the audience thinking, excited, concerned, desirous to hear more, read more, or do something about what was said. It should meet all the criteria listed below for the *average* and *above average* speeches and also match the following description:

1. It constitutes a genuinely individual contribution by the speaker to the knowledge or beliefs of the audience.
2. It meets the assignment exactly.
3. It contains elements of vividness and special interest in the use of language.
4. It is delivered in a fluent, polished manner that strengthens the impact of the speaker's message.
5. It illustrates mastery of the use of connectives.
6. It exhibits creative thinking about and logical analysis of the topic.

An *above average* **(B)** speech is a good speech. It has significant content, good organization, and proficient delivery. It should meet all of the criteria for the *average* speech and also match the following description:

1. It fulfills all major functions of a speech introduction and conclusion.
2. It displays clear organization of main points and support materials.
3. Its main points are supported with evidence that meets the tests of accuracy, relevance, objectivity, and sufficiency.
4. It exhibits proficient use of connectives.
5. It is delivered skillfully enough so as not to distract attention from the speaker's message.
6. It demonstrates skill in winning understanding of challenging concepts, events, objects or processes; or in either winning agreement from auditors initially inclined toward apathy or disagreement or in winning action from auditors.

An *average* **(C)** speech is an adequate speech. It is usually organized and clear, but it may lack audience impact or interest, strong support material, sustained eye contact, and effective non-verbal delivery. It should match the following description:

1. It conforms to the kind of speech assigned.
2. It is ready for presentation on the assigned date.
3. It meets the time limit.
4. It fulfills any special requirements of the assignment--such as preparing an outline, using a visual aid, or citing the appropriate number and type of sources. [See assignment sheets for these criteria.]
5. It has a clear specific purpose and central idea.

14

6. It has an identifiable introduction, body, and conclusion.
7. It follows one of the patterns of organization reasonably well.
8. It shows reasonable directness and competence in delivery.
9. It is free of repeated errors in grammar, pronunciation, and word usage.

As is clear from the criteria, completing a speaking assignment in a timely way following the requirements and guidelines discussed in your textbook, in lecture and in lab will typically result in a speech that earns a C or better. But, as on an exam, it is possible to earn lower grades on speeches.

A *below average* (D) speech is deficient in significant ways. It is characterized by one or more of the following:

1. It fails to clearly conform to any of the patterns of organization.
2. It is delivered in a way that ignores the audience (e.g., it is read to the audience).
3. It is delivered late with prior approval of your instructor.
4. It fails to conform to the time limit.
5. It fails to use or cite support materials as required by the assignment.
6. It does not conform to specific requirements of the assignment.

A *failing* (F) speech is seriously deficient and is characterized by one or more of the following:

1. It is not delivered on the day assigned and the speaker has not contacted his/her instructor prior to class.
2. It has serious ethical flaws such as plagiarizing another person's speech, using sources without proper citation, or manufacturing support material and citations.
3. It does not correspond to the definition of the assignment (e.g., it is persuasive when the assignment calls for an informative speech).
4. It does not come close to conforming to the time limit.
5. It insults, humiliates, or demeans the audience or members of the community at large or is in other ways inappropriate for a presentation in a university classroom.

In addition to her experience with the public speaking course, the author relied on the following sources when creating this list of grading criteria: Oliver, Robert. "The Eternal (And Infernal) Problem of Grades." The Speech Teacher, IX (1960): 8-11; Lucas, Stephen. Instructor's Manual to Accompany the Art of Public Speaking. New York: McGraw-Hill, 1995; Dwyer, Karen. Public Speaking Workbook. New York: McGraw-Hill, 1996; and Atkins, Martha. "Fundamentals of Speech Communication," course packet, ISU, Spring 1993.

INTRODUCTORY SPEECH ASSIGNMENT

This is a <u>two minute</u> speech of self-introduction. The purpose of this assignment is to give you a chance to "break the ice" with the audience. Begin your speech by introducing yourself (name, year, major and hometown at least) then develop the body of your speech according to one of the following descriptions.

1. Bring in an object that represents who you are or would like to be. Include in your talk, how the object represents you. If the object is too large to bring (or is not allowed on campus such as weapons or live animals), you may use a picture or a model. Remember, we are not interested in the object itself, but rather in what the object reveals about <u>you</u>.

Or,

2. Give a speech where you answer the question: What new and/or unusual events occurred on your birthday? Talk to your family or go to the library and read a newspaper from the day and year you were born. Create your speech by using information that you find interesting and that will tell the audience a little about who you are.

Or,

3. Give a speech where you introduce yourself to the audience by focusing on one of your unusual traits. Tell us about the trait and how it affects your life in significant ways. Aim for the unusual [common traits that **do not** work well include things such as: I like talking to my friends, my family is important to me, I study hard, I love movies/video games/music/sports, or I am from someplace that is not unusual]. Unusual traits will help us understand more about your character and what distinguishes you from others.

Or,

4. Give a speech that explains an event, a decision, or an accomplishment of which you are proud. Perhaps it was a moment of success in meeting a particular challenge or a time when you felt that you had moved beyond the typical human state of egocentrism. Such a speech is typically a narrative, but be sure to pull the parts together or to tell the moral of the story as well so that the point you want the audience to learn about you is clear.

Advice:

1. Plan the speech and rehearse it. You will want to leave the audience with a good impression of you. You also want to begin to get used to speaking within a time limit.

2. Organize your ideas. Make sure the speech has an introduction, body, and a conclusion.

3.   Deliver the speech from one 4" x 6" note card with just key ideas on it. This will be the best way to practice for the speeches to come--and you know the topic very well.

4.   Aim to address the audience with as much eye contact as possible.

Assessment: This speech will give the chance of getting some quick simple feedback on some of the speaking skills you bring into the class. Your Lab instructor will look for the following issues:

____ Did the speaker have an introduction? ____ Body? ____ Conclusion?
____ Did the speaker express ideas in an orderly way?
____ Did the speaker maintain audience attention with content? ____ delivery?
____ Did the speaker have good eye contact with the audience?
____ Did the speaker avoid filling pauses with words such as "like," "you know," "um," "uh," or "and"?
____ Did the speaker use vocal variation?
____ Did the speaker use hands effectively?
____ Did the speaker use good posture and have a confident stance?
____ Did the speaker have facial animation?
____ Was the flow of words smooth and uninterrupted?
____ Did the speaker put the audience at ease?

Unit I: Informative Speaking

Paired Perspectives: Brief Informative Speech Assignment

Purposes:
- To explore structural elements and organizational patterns for informative speeches and apply them.
- To experience delivering an informative speech with a partner before delivering one solo.
- To meet and work with classmates to help build class community.

Assignment: You will plan, prepare, and deliver a brief informative speech with a partner. The speech will inform the audience about two different perspectives on a topic.

Topic Choices:
- It can be a pro-con speech where one speaker explains why someone might support one perspective and the other explains why another person supports an opposing view. For example, one might explain why some parents/experts choose to spank their children and the other speaker explains why some parents/experts choose not to spank, or the pair might explain their different views on gun control or capital punishment.

- It can be a speech sharing each speaker's unique perspective on the same topic or issue. For example, each speaker might share ideas about how to resolve roommate conflicts; each speaker might give a different interpretation of a movie, book, TV ad, or piece of art; each speaker might share a family or cultural practice such as how birthdays or holidays are celebrated; each speaker might share about their heroes or the person with whom they would most like to have dinner and conversation and why. Or you can go for an easy topic like having each speaker explain his or her choice of major or living arrangements.

Requirements:
- The speech will be 4 minutes in length (time window +/- 1 min.); topic form must be submitted to your Lab Instructor.
- The speech should contain the following parts of an informative speech as explained in your Lucas text: introduction with CARRP, two main points, connective statements throughout, conclusion.
- The speech will be delivered by both partners. Each speaker will deliver one main point and either the introduction or the conclusion - using one notecard or half sheet of paper.
- A draft outline for the speech, using the format in the workbook, with the parts each of you will do labeled (*see sample on next page*)
- A specific purpose and central idea must be submitted with the outline draft.

Sample Draft of Outline [turn the page to see a complete sample outline]:

Introduction *written out in paragraph form with CARRP parts labeled*   N. Johnson
and speaker name placed at right as shown.
Typical Order of CARRP in an Introduction is:
> *Attention*
> *Reveal Topic*
> *Credibility*
> *Relate to Audience*
> *Preview*

[Connective: Signpost "We will start with Josie talking about…"]

I. Main Point   J. Smith
> *A. Sub point*
> *B. Sub point*

[Connective: Transition "Now that we know about…, Nate will discuss…"]

II. Main Point   N. Johnson
> *A. Sub point*
> *B. Sub point*

Conclusion *Written out in paragraph form with required parts labeled.*   J. Smith
Typical order of Conclusion parts is:
> *Signal the End*
> *Reinforce Central Idea (often by a creative summary)*
> *Clear Closing Line*

Additional specifics:

1. Each person should have equal responsibility for preparing and delivering this speech.
2. Delivery should be extemporaneous, one note card/half sheet limit for each speaker.
3. Grading will focus on the structure of the presentation, including smooth transitions from speaker to speaker.
4. Integrating evidence with oral citations is not required, but can earn a bonus point if good sources are used well.

Paired Perspectives Speech Sample Outline

Specific Purpose: To inform our audience about the holidays our families celebrate to excess.

Central Idea: The 4th of July and Halloween are holidays our families celebrate in surprising ways.

Pattern of Organization: Topical

Introduction   **Matt Ang**

  I. **(Attention Getter)** Does your family have a favorite holiday? Thanksgiving? St. Patrick's Day? Christmas? Hanukah? Birthdays?

  II. **(Reveal Topic)** Most families have some holidays they ignore or just treat as three day weekends and others that require extensive planning and preparation. We found that our families have a quirk of putting lots of energy into what some consider second tier holidays—

  III. **(Relate to Audience)** you know the kind of holiday you didn't even get a day off of grade school to celebrate.

  IV. **(Credibility)** Through experience and conversations with others, we have both learned that our families are unusual in the energy they put into some celebrations.

  V. **(Preview)** Today, we'll tell you how we celebrate the 4th of July and Halloween so you can see that even these lowly holidays can build great family memories.

Connective: (Signpost) First, Abby, will share her red, white and blue family traditions.

Perspective I   **Abby Stone**

I. In my family the 4th of July is the holiday that is celebrated with surprising energy.

  A. Part of our celebration has to do with the fact that my hometown Garnavillo, IA goes all out.

      1. There is always a big parade and my family always participates in some creative way.

      2. My family members have often won the kids pedal pull contest held after the parade.

      3. The city fireworks would not be complete without the sparklers we bring.

  B. My family always has a reunion along with the 4th of July celebration so we have invented other traditions centered on competition.

      1. My cousins and I compete for the most patriotic look while my mom and aunts apparently compete for the most patriotic dessert.

      2. The old vs. young volleyball is an annual event.

      3. My uncle seems to want to compete with the city for fireworks displays.

Connective (Transition): While my family is red white and blue all the way through, Matt's family doesn't even always head out for fireworks. Instead they put their energy into celebrating Halloween.

You'll need a connective of some type between each main point. The transition is the most common kind.

Perspective II   **Matt Ang**

II. In my family Halloween is the holiday that is celebrated with surprising energy.
    A. It started with elaborate costumes since no hobo or purchased superhero outfits were good enough.
        1. When we were younger my mom made papier-mâché heads for three bears costumes.
        2. Another year my dad talked us into dressing up like the rock band Kiss.
    B. As we got older we stopped dressing up ourselves and started decorating the house.
        1. We've got great scary things all over the yard and by the door.
        2. We play that spooky music.
        3. One time we pretended to be stuffed dummies set up in chairs with candy bowls on our laps.

Connective: (Internal Summary): When I was a kid it was fun to dress up for trick or treat and have people give me lots of candy because my costume was so great, but now I like to go home to help my brother make ours the most interesting scary house on the block.

Conclusion   **Abby Stone**

I. **Signal the End:** As you can see, our families really invest time, energy and money into these different holidays.
II. **Reinforce the Central Idea:** My family really goes all out for the 4th of July parades and foods and contests and Matt's family had to build an extra shed to store Halloween decorations. Probably your family has some other holiday that brings you great memories.
III. **Clear Closing Line:** Whether it's patriotism or getting candy or observing religious celebrations, we hope each of your families has some holiday that brings you great memories too.

These speakers relied on their own experience and did not cite any sources, so they did not need a bibliography. If you integrate sources into your speech to develop an idea more powerfully, you would need a bibliography. For later speeches this will be required.

23

Feedback Form for the Paired Perspectives Speech

Speaker Names: _____

Introduction:
        ____ Attention step?
        ____ Topic revealed?
        ____ Credibility built?
        ____ Related to the audience?
        ____ Preview of the Body?

Structure:
        ____ Did the speakers clearly move from the introduction to the Body?
        ____ Did the speakers clearly move from one main point to the next?
        ____ Did the speakers clearly move from the Body to the Conclusion?

Conclusion:
        ____ Did the speakers clearly signal the end?
        ____ Did the speakers clearly reinforce the central idea?

Format and Clarity:
        ____ Did the speech meet the assignment requirements? [time, single note card, two perspectives]
        ____ Did the speakers share responsibilities and present as a team?
        ____ Did the speakers turn in a clear outline with appropriate labels?
        ____ Did the specific purpose pass the tests for specific purposes?
        ____ Did the central idea pass the tests for central ideas?

_____ Classwork pts. earned for this speech (+___ bonus for integrating quality research)

****

Extra feedback

____ Did the speakers use extemporaneous delivery?
____ Did the speakers maintain audience attention with content?
____ Did the speakers maintain audience attention with delivery?

Observations about the speaker's presentation of self:

      eye contact

      voice

      gestures/stance/facial expressiveness

      appropriate appearance

The Informative Speech Assignment and Requirements

1. The Topic Form and discussion for the Informative Speech must be submitted through Blackboard to your lab instructor by the deadline indicated on the syllabus. Be sure to visit the site later to look at the feedback on your topic form. You have three basic areas from which to choose a topic:

Option A: "An interesting concept or process from my major." This is an informative speech that helps people outside your area of expertise understand some <u>specific aspect</u> of what people who work in your field know that people outside your field would be enlightened by knowing, So dig into something related to your major that could interest a general audience. This might include topics such as: "To inform my audience how a meteorologist uses Doppler Radar"; "To inform my audience about the discipline strategies teachers use in the classroom"; "To inform my audience how architects incorporate landscape into their designs"; "To inform my audience how to read a stock report." Some students have chosen to inform the audience about research conducted in their field. Sample specific purpose statements along this line include: "To inform my audience about research showing how people actually use computers"; "To inform my audience about research on the effects of advertising on children." Give a speech that makes it easy for the listener to answer the "so what?" question. Speeches that just list career options or coursework for your major are NOT appropriate; tell us something specific and intriguing about what you are learning. Typical resources for such a speech would include library books, textbooks, lectures, journals in your field, and websites of professional organizations in your area of study.

Option B: "One of the most interesting things I have learned in my college coursework." This is an informative speech that gives you an opportunity to find out more about a topic that you found very interesting when you first heard about it. The challenge is to help someone not already interested become so and to help your classmates learn something new. This might include topics that came up in your non-major coursework in lectures, during a project or in your reading. For example: "To inform my audience about the debate over who wrote Shakespeare's plays"; or "To inform my audience about creation myths from three different cultures"; or "To inform my audience about the pressure dynamics that allow airplanes to lift off the ground"; or "To inform my audience about theories of personality formation." Typical resources for such a speech would include library books, textbooks, lectures, journals in the field, and websites of professional organizations in the relevant area of study.

Option C: "Fascinating Communication Issues and Concepts." Our textbook is an introductory text focused on public speaking, but the field of communication is complex and diverse. Is there a communication topic you want to know more about? Research it and share it with your classmates. Don't insult the audience by giving a speech about how to give a good speech, but try out different Specific Purpose Statements such as: "To inform my audience of the different meanings of non-verbal signs across cultures"; or "To inform my audience about the debate over the use of PowerPoint in professional settings"; or "To inform my audience how to avoid miscommunication"; or "To inform my audience how visualization reduces speaking anxiety;" or "To inform my audience about the debates concerning hate speech on college campuses." Typical resources for such a speech would include library resources, textbooks, lectures, communication journals, and websites of professional communicators and communication organizations. Looking for topics? Follow-up on a footnote in the textbook or check out ComAbstracts in our Library's list of Indexes.

2. The time limit for the speech is 6 minutes. You should time your speech as you practice it so that you are sure that it falls within a minute on either side of this time limit. The full minute window on either side of the 6 minute limit gives you plenty of time to add an aside or restate a point as needed while you speak. Failure to meet the time limit will result in a 1/3 letter grade penalty that will increase at 30 second intervals [so the first penalties begin at 4:59 and 7:01, the next 1/3 deduction is added at 4:29 and at 7:30, etc.]

3. Use of a visual aid is required. Visual aids can increase your confidence and can help maintain the attention of the audience as well as increase their understanding of the subject. Follow the guidelines in chapter 13 and your Lab Instructor's advice as you select or create appropriate visual aids. Failure to include a visual aid will result in a 1/3 letter grade penalty, but more important, you will lose a great tool to engage your audience and improve your delivery.

4. Use of at least three strong sources is required. We expect college level sources—use the tools that you learned about in Library 160 or in your English classes; not just Google searches (see "Source Requirements and Orally Citing Sources for the Informative Speech" below for more details). These sources, be they books, articles, or individuals, must be cited orally in the speech and included in a bibliography at the end of your outline. Failure to cite sources orally will result in a 1/3 letter grade penalty for each source left out, such that a speech without source citations would be graded down a full letter grade. Failure to cite sources properly orally or in the bibliography or choosing to cut and paste together an outline (even with citations) may result in a plagiarism or academic dishonest inquiry (for citation help, see "Sample Source Citation Guide for Bibliographies" below).

5. Delivery of the speech is to be extemporaneous—from no more than five (one-sided) note cards. Give the speech from a brief speaking outline, not from memory, manuscript, or full sentence outline. Failure to deliver the speech from a speaking outline will have an impact on the success of the speech (and so, on your grade).

6. Two copies of a typed complete draft of your outline are due on your workshop day as indicated on the syllabus.

7. A typed final preparation outline is due at the beginning of your lab section on your assigned speaking day **and must be uploaded to the course Blackboard site** by the end of that day. Failure to give your speech on the day assigned can mean failing the assignment. Be in contact with your lab instructor before missing a speech!

Whatever direction you choose to take in the speech, you need to remember that you are addressing a general audience: how can you best relate to and interest them in what interests you? Chapter 14 of the textbook contains information concerning building the informative speech. In addition to meeting these requirements, the major grading criteria for the speech are: structure (including introduction, main points, connectives, and conclusion); clarity (in form and content); full and interesting development of ideas new to the audience; relating to/adapting to/involving the audience; and delivery skills. See the following page for the feedback form your instructor will use when grading.

Informative Speech Feedback Form

Speaker _____

Topic _____

Guide: O-outstanding S-satisfactory N–needs work

		Comments
Introduction		
Attention and Interest	O S N	
Revealed Topic	O S N	
Established Credibility	O S N	
Related to the audience	O S N	
Previewed the body	O S N	
Effective delivery of the intro	O S N	

Body
Main points clear	O S N
Pattern of Organization helpful	O S N
Support materials adequate	O S N
Content accurate, interesting	O S N
Language use strong	O S N
Connectives effective	O S N
Visual aid content strong	O S N

Conclusion
Prepared audience for ending	O S N
Reinforced the Central Idea	O S N
Effective delivery of the conc.	O S N

Delivery
Maintained eye contact	O S N
Used voice effectively	O S N
Facial expression effective	O S N
Gestures effective	O S N
Stance strong	O S N
Visual aid presentation strong	O S N

Overall Evaluation
Topic challenging	O S N
Speech adapted to this audience	O S N
Presentation of self strong	O S N
Speech fit the assignment	O S N

For Next Time:

Meeting Source Requirements and Using Sources Well for the Informative Speech

1. The Informative speech requires a minimum of 3 good sources. How do you know if you are using good sources? The textbook discussion in chapters 6 and 7 offer much guidance. There are four central questions to ask about your sources.
   - Question #1: **Expertise?** Does the person who wrote this know what he/she is talking about?
   - Question #2: **Bias?** Does the person who wrote this have financial or ideological interests which significantly distort his/her judgment?
   - Question #3: **Reviewed?** Did anyone else spend time figuring out if this was good information?
   - Question #4: **Recency?** Is the source up to date given the topic?

   In addition to the general principles governing good use of supporting material, the following guidelines cover how we count sources in this course.

2. Speeches must be supported with documentation from reputable sources. These sources of your support material <u>must be identified out loud</u> during your speech. For example:

   "According to <u>Business Week</u> in March of 2008, for every 7 patients who suffer an injury because of medical negligence, only one will file a malpractice claim."

   (See below for more examples of oral citations of sources.)

3. Magazines, newspapers, books, pamphlets (from legitimate, respected organizations), journals or interviews (only one interview "counts" per speech), may all be used as sources. Some of these sources can now be accessed through the Web. In this course we distinguish between simple web sites (the kind accessible through a Google search, which can have very weak credibility) and Internet access to material that has been reviewed by people in the field (strong credibility). Often these are websites that contain material also available in published resources, such as http://jama.ama-assn.org which gives you access to the highly-respected <u>Journal of the American Medical Association</u> on-line. Using the web accessible materials available through the Iowa State Library's Instruction Library Guides [aka Class Guides] pages devoted to SpCm 212 can help you to reach strong research sources. You'll find a link to our SpCm 212 Library Guide on our Blackboard site.

4. All of your citations for the speech cannot come from the same type of source, i.e. all magazines, all books, all newspapers or all web sites.

5. Dictionaries and general encyclopedias (including Britannica and Wikipedia), while helpful in providing background information, <u>will not</u> count as sources for the speeches.

6. Judging the quality of the sources you choose is important. Weak source material—web sites prepared by unknown people who may just be making things up, or prepared by elementary teachers for use by third graders, or entertainment media (movies, TV, humor columns in newspapers) as a source for facts, or the <u>Daily</u> for national and international issues—can hurt your credibility, can lead you to provide false information to your audience, and, in the end, will hurt the assessment of your speech. Internet sources are particularly challenging to judge. See chapter 6 in the textbook for advice about searching for and evaluating Internet resources.

7. In addition to citing the sources orally in your speeches, you must include a bibliography of all sources used at the end of your preparation outline. For example:

    Jetson, George. "Are Malpractice suits Really Killing America's Hospitals?" <u>Business Week</u>. March 17, 2009, pp. 27-29.

    The following pages include examples of citation styles to use on your preparation outline. Our course website also has materials to support the development of your bibliography.

8. **The bottom line: Failure to orally cite at least the minimum number of sources for the speech assignment will lead to a grade deduction for the speech.** Use of sources without oral citations or with improper bibliographic citation on outlines is a problem. Improper use of sources—simple cutting and pasting together the prose of others with or without minor changes—even with citation of some sort, can still go against the expectation that speakers work with materials & develop expertise before speaking. Any of these problems can lead to lower grades or even plagiarism or academic dishonesty discussions.

Here are some examples of <u>oral citations</u> of sources.

In **informative speeches** the audience wants some assurance that you are using quality resources that ought to be believed, but since you aren't trying to change their minds the oral citations do not need elaborate details. The oral citation should provide enough information that your listeners can judge the credibility of the source for the claim made and could ask you to provide more information about the sources at the end of your speech.

"The <u>Wall Street Journal</u> reported last year that Ford is now hiring more college-educated people to work on its assembly lines."

"According to Dr. Claude Frazier, entomologist at the University of Washington, not only do house dust mites live in dust, but also in particles of human and animal dander, kapok, and cotton lint commonly found in rugs, furniture, box springs, mattresses, draperies, and any other place where a large number of dead human skin cells can be found."

[cite for a visual aid] "Consider this picture supplied by Allergy Control Products on their web site, which illustrates the ideal dust mite-free bedroom."

"According to a 2009 report from the National Safety Council, choking is the sixth leading cause of accidental death and is responsible for nearly 3,900 deaths per year."

"In her book, <u>The Imposter Phenomenon</u>, Dr. Pauline Rose Clance explains that the fear of failure invades our lives. Dr. Clance claims that...."

"The April 2007 edition of <u>Prevention</u> magazine included an interesting example of a serious allergic reaction. This young man had very few symptoms of any type of allergy while living at home, but after moving into his college dormitory...."

"According the official website of the U.S. Bureau of Indian Affairs, one of the first acts of the Continental Congress in 1775 was to establish a Committee on Indian Affairs."

Sample Source Citation Guide for Bibliographies

The following references are examples of what your citations should look like on your References page. Remember, the goal of good citations is to lead others to more information.

Electronic Sources

Expanded Academic Index ASAP Articles

Author. "Article Title." *Journal Title* Volume (Date Published): Page Range. Database. Vendor. Date Accessed. <Web Address>.

Lehrer, Eli. "Cities Combat Violent Crime." *Insight on the News* 15 (19 July 1999): 14. Expanded Academic Index ASAP. Gale Group. 5 October, 1999. <http://infotrac.galegroup.com/itweb/iastu_main>.

Journal Articles Online

Author(s). "Article Title." *Journal Title* Volume (Year Published): Page Range. Date Accessed <Web Address>.

Baker Graham, Margaret, and Neil Lindeman. "The Rhetoric and Politics of Science in the Case of the Missouri River System." *Journal of Business and Technical Communication* 19(2005): 422-49. 29 May 2005 <http://proxy.lib.iastate.edu:2591/pqdweb?index>.

Newspaper Articles Online

Author(s). "Article Title." *Newspaper Title* Date Published. Date Accessed <Web Address>.

Hutchinson, Sue. "Some Chick Lit Provides More Than Empty Calories." *Mercury News* 24 May 2006. 29 May 2006 <http://web116.epnet.com/citation.asp?>.

Websites

- *hint:* Beware of dot com sites as they hold little credibility in formal citations.

Page or Website Title. Date Last Updated. Organization/Author. Date Accessed <Web Address>.

Key Facts about Mumps. 14 April 2006. Center for Disease Control. 24 May 2006 <http://www.cdc.gov/nip/diseases/mumps/vac-chart.htm>.

New Form for Citation of Online Sources from the newest style manuals eliminates the use of URLs entirely. You can use this system if it is what you learned. Here is an example:

"Estimates for the Total Number of IDPs for all of Sudan" (as of January 2010). Internal Displacement Monitoring Centre. 22 February 2010. Web. 20 July 2010.

TV or Radio Programs

"Segment Title." Narrator. *Series Title*. Network Name. Station Call Letters. Broadcast Place. Broadcast Date.

"Yes . . . but is it Art?" Narr. Morley Safer. *Sixty Minutes*. CBS. WCBS. New York. 19 Sept. 1993.

Paper Sources

Books
Author(s). *Title*. Place of Publication: Publisher, Date Published.

McLuhan, Marshall. *The Guttenberg Galaxy*. Toronto: University of Toronto Press, 1962.

Alternatively, the newest stylebooks add Print at the end of the publishing information to indicate that you examined the work in hard copy not online:
Steidle, Brian, and Gretchen Steidle Wallace. *The Devil Came on Horseback*. New York: Public Affairs, 2007. Print.

Journal Articles
Author(s). "Article Title." *Journal Title* Volume (Date Published): Page Range.

Norris, Elaine. "Age Matters in a Feminist Classroom." *National Women's Studies Association Journal* 18(2006): 61-84.

Lectures and Speeches
Lecturer/Speaker. "Title of Lecture/Speech." Venue. Date of Lecture/Speech.

Chomsky, Noam. "Global Justice and Human Rights." Iowa State University. 11 Apr. 2006.

Magazine Articles
Author(s). "Article Title." *Magazine Title*. Date of Publication: Page Range.

Weintraub, Arlene, and Laura Cohen. "A Thousand-Year Plan for Nuclear Waste." *Business Week* 6 May 2002: 94-6.

Newspaper Articles
Author(s). "Article Title." *Newspaper Title*. Date of Publication: Page Range.

Harris, Nicole. "Airports in the Throes of Change." *Wall Street Journal* 27 Mar. 2002: B1+.

Pamphlets
Title of Pamphlet. Place of Publication: Publisher, Date of Publication.

Renoir Lithographs. New York: Dover, 1994.

Personal and Email Interviews
Interviewee. Credential. Type of Interview. Date of Interview.

Maddox, Jennifer. Director of Creative Writing Department. Personal interview. 11 Jan. 2006.

Harle, Marissa. Director of Chemistry Department. Email interview. 7 Dec. 2005.

Sample Informative Speech Outline: Dictionaries

The following outline is a pair of outlines—a <u>final complete outline</u> followed by a sample set of note cards used as <u>a speaking outline</u>. They can be used as models for preparing your outlines for the Informative speech.

Rachel McKenny
Speech Com 212
Spring 2011
Lab Section # 13 and Lab Instructor's name: Abby Stonner

Specific Purpose Statement: To inform my audience about the history of English language dictionaries from the late 1600s to today.

Central Idea: English language dictionaries have gone through three main periods of transformation from the beginnings of dictionaries with early printing, through the first full dictionaries in the 1900s, and into the modern, technological, era.

> Note how the SP and CI follow the chapter 4 rules for phrasing each of these statements. The Central Idea indicates the 3 main points of the speech. Each main point refers to a development of the Dictionary in historical time which means this speech is organized chronologically.

Pattern of Organization: Chronological

Introduction:

I. **Attention:** Think of a word. Any word. Trust me on this. Close your eyes and think. There's very little chance that the person on the right or left of you thought of the same word. According to the Oxford English Dictionary, there are over 200,000 words in the English language: enough for a different word for every man, woman, and child in Des Moines.

II. **Reveal Topic:** Whether your word was unicorn, economics, airplane, or none of the above, your word was in my word. The word I was thinking of is "dictionary."

III. **Credibility and Goodwill:** As an English major, I took a course on the History of English where we studied the beginnings of these dictionaries, and my interest in this nerdy subject has only increased with the other linguistics courses I've taken.

IV. **Relate to Audience:** Whether English is your first language or your eighth, there's a good chance you've used a dictionary at some point in your life. Perhaps it was that very aggressive scrabble game with your parents. Maybe it was in your attempt to understand vocabulary in this course.

V. **Preview:** Perhaps when you hear dictionary, you think boring. If so, I'm going to prove you wrong. Today I'll show you what this great book means to you through the humble origins of the dictionary from the 1400s, the first comprehensive dictionaries through the 1900s, and what we have now in the 21st century.

(Internal Preview): English dictionaries begin with the letter A, but the beginnings of the history of the English dictionary starts with P for printing press.

> Note how each main point and sub point is a single complete sentence.

I. English Dictionaries owe their existence to an invention of the mid-1400s.

    A. Johannes Gutenberg is the super hero of this story.

        1. He didn't have super powers, but he did invent the machine that started the Renaissance: the Printing Press.

        2. Today we don't think of these machines as anything special, but imagine having to write your homework in wax blocks or on animal hides.

Note how the credibility of this source is made clear.

a. According to Dr. Susan Yager, Middle English professor here at Iowa State, that was the common form.

b. You all have Johannes Gutenberg to thank for those printers in your dorm room and computer labs.

B.   Without the ability to mass produce texts, we wouldn't have started to solidify our language.

Including the source citation on the outline helps make sure you remember to cite it when you speak.

1.   Spelling in English was not standardized through the 1700s.

2.   Without standardization, it was hard to teach English since we didn't have a language that everyone could read.

3.   Albert Bough and Thomas Cable write in their textbook, A History of the English Language that there were five ways to write the word "fellow"!

C.   People began to see that it would be easier to have standard forms of words. So, dictionaries of 'hard words' began to be printed.

D.   Some early dictionaries printed in England were bilingual.

1.   You might use something similar today to look up the word "fork" in Spanish (It's 'tenedor!')

2.   Many English words that we use today came from other languages like German, French, and Latin.

E.   There were even slang dictionaries.

1.   The one I'm showing you attempted to collect the slang of the "gypsies, beggars, thieves and cheats."

2.   Did you know the word "chitchat" existed in 1699? According to this dictionary, sailors used it to mean meaningless talk back and forth.

(**Transition:** These were all specialized dictionaries, however. While Guttenberg's invention paved the way for the beginning of the expansion of English, we didn't have a real dictionary yet.)

II.   Comprehensive English dictionaries began to emerge in the 1700s and continued through the publication of the Oxford English Dictionary in the twentieth century.

A. Baugh and Cable write that it wasn't until 1755 that Dr. Samuel Johnson took the initiative to print the first comprehensive collection of English words.

Note how each main point has a connective between it and the next main point and each type of connective is properly labeled.

1.   It included around 40,000 words, far less than those 200,000 we have today.

2.   According to an article titled "The Dictionary Makers" by the writer and scholar Anthony Burgess, Johnson not only had definitions and ideas about language, but he imposed his opinions in his dictionary.

3.   It contains insults to political figures and institutions he hated, just like Simon Cowell might do if he wrote a textbook.

B. The Oxford English Dictionary, which has become our standard, was published for the first time in 1928.

1.   Unlike Samuel Johnson, who was a scholar, the writers of the OED, as it is called, came from all walks of life.

2.   The leader of the OED project was a man named James Murray who never even graduated from college!

3.   Murray only got to the letter T before his death, but by 1989 when the second version came out, there were 20 large volumes filled with words.

(**Internal Summary**: Without Samuel Johnson and James Murray the English language would have stood still. Their vast collections of words became a strong foundation for our language study. **Transition:** But the story of the dictionary doesn't end with the 1900s, technology has given rise to new 21st century dictionaries.)

III. English Dictionaries today have been dramatically shaped by technology.
   A.   Now, even more popular than those twenty-volume whales of words, we have online versions of the dictionaries.
      1. Catharine Soanes is the current head of Online Dictionaries for Oxford University Press, and in a recent interview she stated that 2,000 new words were added in the newest edition her dictionary, including "staycation," "vuvuzela," and "turducken."
      2. A lot of these words, says Soanes, came from the internet and social networking.
         a. "Tweeting" is in the dictionary now, and even "bromance."
         b. Online Dictionaries show the staying power in words, even ones that arise from "Superbad."
   B.   New technology has created new words and new ways for them to be tracked.
      1. The Urban Dictionary is completely run by the people online, voting on popular definitions of made-up words.
         a. An internet coma means you have stared at your computer for hours and hours.
         b. Facebook fever is the word for someone who checks Facebook every six minutes.
         c. What's amazing is that these words catch on, and begin to be used in everyday language!
      2. Urban Dictionary was started by Aaron Peckham in 1999.
         a. Its first definition, according to the New York Times, was "the man."
         b. With four million definitions already and thousands new every day, this is a testament to how fast the language can change when people put their minds to it.

Conclusion:

I. **Signal the End:** Though we've talked about a lot of movements today, from writing on animal hides to voting for new words on Urban Dictionary, I hope you've learned something about how our language works.

II. **Restate Central Idea**: While in the beginning it was innovators like Gutenberg, Johnson, and Murray, today dictionaries are formed from everyday people and their creativity.

III. **Clear Closing line:** When working on your Informative Speeches, you'll all be using a lot of words. Those words came from somewhere: whether formed from other languages, or created for slang usage by old sailors or urban hipsters. Think about your words. Choose them carefully. Each one of those 200,000 words can be really powerful, if you know how to use them. Thank you.

Bibliography
Baugh, Albert C., and Thomas Cable. A History of the English Language. Englewood Cliffs, NJ: Prentice-Hall, 1978. Print.

Burgess, Anthony. "The Dictionary Makers." The Wilson Quarterly 17.3 (1993): 104-10. JSTOR. Web. 17 Feb. 2011.

"Des Moines QuickFacts." State and County QuickFacts. US Census Bureau, 8 July 2009. Web. 20 Feb. 2011.

'Turducken,' 'Vuvuzela,' And More New Dictionary Words. 22 Aug. 2010. Weekend Edition. National Public Radio. Web. Jan.-Feb. 2011. Transcript.

Urban Dictionary. Web. 18 Feb. 2011.

Yager, Susan. "Chaucer and Writing." Iowa State University. 21 Feb. 2011. Lecture.

Speaking Notes/Outline

10 Suggestions:

1. Use 4 x 6 index cards and write on only one side.

2. Use as few words as possible, but keep direct quotes, statistics, and source citations.

3. Make notes readable at a glance using large printing or a large font size and using pen rather than pencil.

4. Number your note cards so you can get them back in order quickly.

5. Use highlighters or different colors of ink to draw your eye to essential parts (such as using yellow highlighters to signal all source citations).

6. Write in delivery cues to help you remember to look up, to take a good pause, or to slow down. Make sure your comments are phrased in a positive way.

7. Be sure to make a note to yourself about when you should show your visual aid to the audience.

8. Use outline symbols or at least indentations to help you keep track of the order of ideas.

9. Don't make the cards too crowded.

10. Use the cards as sparingly as possible; do not read your notes to the audience.

Below are some sample note cards such as the speaker might have used for the Dictionary speech. These speaking notes show the contrast between the preparation outline, on previous pages in the workbook, and the Speaking outline or notes.

1

INTRO

    Think of a word... According to <u>OED</u> 200,000 words... men, woman, children in Des Moines

    Whatever your word was airplane, economics, unicorn... your word was in my word... (**slide switch**)

Interest in this nerdy subject: Undergrad? Linguistics at ISU?

Whether English is your 1st language or your 8th... scrabble? vocab?

    PAUSE

PREVIEW: Perhaps when you hear dictionary you think boring. If so... humble origins in the 1400s, the compellation of the first complete dictionaries through the 1900s, and in the modern era. (**switch**)

BREATHE!

2

Internal Preview: ("Just like all English D.'s begin with the letter "A"...")

I. Dictionary didn't always exist: innovators

Superhero Guttenberg (**click three times to get all effects up,** <u>check screen</u>)

- Invention in Germany affects us today?
- <u>**Susan Yager, Middle English prof at ISU,**</u> "Animal hides /wax blocks"
- Relate to audience: Printers in dorm rooms, thank Guttenberg!

Look Up! "Without the ability to mass produce text we wouldn't have solidified our language"
(**click**)

- 1700s—many different spellings
- <u>**Albert Bough and Thomas Cable in History of the English Language**</u> (**click to fellow slide**, <u>point out different versions</u>)

Early editions of dictionaries:

- "Dictionaries of hard words" to help learn/teach English
- Bilingual dictionaries (relate to audience with today's use)

Transition: **"These were specialized dictionaries, however. It wasn't until the 1700s that we had our first *comprehensive* dictionaries."**

II. People stepped forward: (**click to slide of Sam/James**)

- <u>**Bough and Cable**</u> write that 1755- Samuel Johnson
  - ○ 40,000 words versus the 200,000 today
  - ○ <u>**Dictionary Makers by scholar and writer Anthony Burgess**</u> put in his own opinions in the definitions
  - ○ Relate: Like Simon Cowell!

SLOW DOWN!

- OED- 1928
  - ○ Unlike SJ, was a collection of not just scholars and linguists but mathematicians, firemen, gardeners...
  - ○ Head of project, James Murray, never graduated from college!
  - ○ Got to letter "T" before death, 20 Volumes in 2nd ed. by 1989

(**click**)

Internal Summary: **"Murray and Johnson's vast collections of words became a strong foundation for our language studies."**

PAUSE

I. Modern age of tech? Computers in our lives
- Apps/Online versus the "20 volume whales of words"
    - **Catherine Soames, online director for the Oxford University Press**, 2,000 words in new edition
    - Staycation, vuvuzela, (**click**) turducken! (explain and connect to audience) (**click**)
    - Social media?—tweet!
    - Media?—bromance! (**click, wait for laugh**)

- Future? How will words be created and changed? (**click**)
    - Urban Dictionary! (relate to audience, have heard of it)
    - **NY Times** wrote that in 1999, Aaron Peckam (first definition "the man")
    - Diseases you might have? (**click**)
        - Internet coma?
        - Facebook fever?

Internal Summary: **"With four million definitions and thousands added every day, this is a testament to what people can do when they put their minds to it!"**

PAUSE   5

CONCLUSION   *(almost there ☺)*

        (**click**)

        "We've talked about a lot of history today" (Signal the end)

               Writing on animal skins—urban dictionary

"While in beginning, innovators like Guttenberg, Johnson, and Murray that paved the way, today _we_ form new words and ideas with our creativity"

Informative speech= no dictionary as a source, but using a lot of words
- Words have meanings
- Words have histories, whether other language or urban hipster
PAUSE—LOOK UP FOR LAST BIT!

CLOSING: **"Think about your words. Choose them carefully. Each of the 200,000 words can be powerful, if you know how to use them."** (**click**)

Bottom line: Prepare note cards early—after practicing with the full outline twice. Reduce to the fewest number of cards and least amount of writing you can, but enough to help you if nerves sneak up on you.

Remember—A speech is NOT a paper standing on its hind legs! The value of the speech is in the presence of the speaker. DON'T read to your classmates. Share what you know in an organized fashion. Focus on the IDEAS of the speech, not on getting the exact WORDS. Giving speeches IS a kind of TALKING. Keep it conversational.

Sample Informative Speech Outline: Dust Bowl

Name: Eric Sims-Brown
Date: February 12, 2009
Lab Section # 13 and Lab Instructor's name: Abby Stonner

Specific Purpose: To inform my audience of the causes and consequences of the Dust Bowl.
Central Idea: We can better respond to current environmental crises by understanding the way humans helped cause the Dust Bowl as well as the impact this environmental disaster had on the population.
Pattern of Organization: Causal

I Attention: Darkness. Your busy day has come to an end. You're thinking of slipping into your pajamas and going to bed. But you're confused. It's not midnight -- it's noon. It's noon and yet everything around you is black. You can't see your hand even though it's only inches from your face. Your house rattles and hisses like a snake. Panicked, your heart racing, you fumble through the dark on your hands and knees. Your breathing is heavy. You crawl, pulling yourself along with your elbows until finally. Finally, you reach what you think is a door. You pull yourself up by the handle. You open the door and see this -- A ten thousand foot high wall of dust traveling at approximately sixty miles an hour.
II. Reveal Topic: The experience I've just described was not uncommon for people living in parts of Nebraska, New Mexico, Colorado, Texas, Oklahoma and Kansas during the 1930's. At that time this area of the country was known as the Dust Bowl.
III. Credibility & Goodwill: Maybe the Dust Bowl seems like an unusual topic, but when I was in high school and had to read John Steinbeck's Grapes of Wrath I became fascinated with the whole idea of huge dust storms right here in America. Now that I am working on my own novel set during this time period, I've had to do more serious research about it.
IV. Relate to the Audience: I've found that the Dust Bowl is considered the greatest environmental disaster in American history. And while this event is in the past, today we face new environmental challenges so it's important for each of us to understand how humans helped create the conditions for this disaster and how awful its effects were.
V. Preview: Today I'll share what I've been learning so you can see first, how the combination of drought and expansion caused the Dust Bowl and then, what the major consequences of these storms were on the region.

(**Connective: Signpost**—I'll start with what caused the Dust Bowl.)

I. The Dust Bowl was created by two main causes.
    A. The first cause of the Dust Bowl was drought.
        1. According to World Climate, an organization that documents historical weather patterns for over 85,000 locations worldwide, typical rainfall in the Great Plains averages eighteen to twenty inches per year.
        2. During the drought in the 1930's yearly rainfall totaled only 9 to 15 inches.

3. Agricultural Historian Douglas Hurt points out that the soil of this region is sandy clay that, when dry, can be easily lifted by the wind.

(**Connective: Internal Preview**: But drought was not unheard of in the Great Plains. So what made the 1930's so unique? Why were the storms during this decade so severe and why did they last so long? The reason is that human expansion and new demands on the land increased the dangerous conditions.)

B. The second main cause of the Dust Bowl was expansion and new demands on the land.
   1. The federal government opened up the Plains to settlement in the late 1800's.
   2. Settlers could claim large tracts of land if they were willing to cultivate it.
      a. Before the turn of the century much of the Great Plains was covered in grass.
      b. This grass had a solid root structure, which helped hold the soil in place.
   3. Ranchers and farmers moved into the region destroying the grasslands.
   4. When wheat prices fell during the Great Depression farmers tried to solve the problem by plowing and planting on more of the land, but that simply exposed more dry soil to the wind.

(**Connective: Transition:** We've seen how drought combined with human expansion and new uses of the land led to the Dust Bowl, now let's take a look at the effects of these storms.)

II. The dust storms of the 1930's had important effects on the land and the people of the Plains.
   A. According to Douglas Hurt, in his book *The Dust Bowl*, the dust storms devastated the land.
      1. An estimated 100 million acres of land throughout the Great Plains was reduced to virtual desert conditions.
      2. That's roughly the same size as Iowa and Minnesota put together
   B. Farmers went bankrupt and many people lost their homes.
   C. Many fled elsewhere in search of jobs and no one moved to the region.
      1. According to the PBS documentary *The American Experience: Surviving the Dust Bowl,* two and a half million people fled the plains states by 1940.
      2. To put that number in perspective, remember that Iowa, today, has only three million residents according to the latest *US Census.*
         a. Can you imagine what it would be like if most of Iowa got up and left?
         b. Or to bring it closer to home, what if 15 people in this room, packed up and left?
   D. The people who stayed faced a tough life.
      1. Dust from the storms affected public health.
         a. Many died from a disease called dust pneumonia.
         b. The Red Cross distributed masks for people to wear.
      2. Dust from the storms also affected everyday life.
         a. Dust seeped into food, water, hair, shoes, bedding -- just about everything.
         b. People continuously had to sweep out their homes and businesses.

      i. Dr. Pamela Rinny-Kehrberg, a history professor here at ISU, in her book *Rooted in Dust* told the story of a janitor in Kansas, who arriving at work, found dirt covering the floor.

     ii. By the end he had removed 37 gallons of dirt.

(**Connective: Internal Summary** - The dust storms of the 1930s damaged millions of acres and lead to a mass exodus. Those who stayed faced health issues. Dust got into everything and made everyday life almost impossible.)

Signal the End: The Dust Bowl is considered the greatest environmental disaster in American history. Today we've learned more about that history.

Reinforce the Central Idea: I've told you how drought and expansion created the dust storms of the 1930's. I've also told you about how these storms impacted the people living in the region.

Clear Closing Line: But why does it matter? Why does this have an impact on you? Because we will continue to face environmental challenges in the years to come. One way we can begin to solve these challenges is by understanding the mistakes we've made in the past and trying our best not to repeat them.

Bibliography

Egan, Timothy. <u>The Worst Hard Time</u>. Houghton-Mifflin Company. 2005. Print.

Hurt, R. Douglas. <u>The Dust Bowl: And Agricultural and Social History.</u> Rowman & Littlefield, 1981. Print.

The American Experience: Surviving the Dust Bowl. WGBH/PBS. 1998. Web.

Rinny-Kehrberg, Pamela. <u>Rooted in Dust</u>. University Press of Kansas, 1997. Print.

World Climate Robert Hoare, Buttle and Tuttle Ltd. Web.

Outline Exercise

In the left-hand column below is a blank outline from a speech about George Washington Carver. In the right-hand column, arranged in random order, are the main points, subpoints, and sub-subpoints to fill in the outline. Choose the appropriate main point, subpoint, or sub-subpoint for each blank in the outline.

Outline	Main points, subpoints, and sub-subpoints
I. 4	1. He developed over 300 products derived from the peanut and 118 from the sweet potato.
A. 3	2. At the end of his career Carver bequeathed his entire estate to Tuskegee to establish a research foundation supporting further scientific exploration.
1. 12	
2. 7	3. As a child, Carver was an ambitious student.
	4. George Washington Carver's years as a student demonstrate his commitment to learning.
B. 9	
1. 10	5. Carver worked at Tuskegee for nearly 50 years making many important discoveries in the field of agriculture.
2. 13	
a. 6	6. At Iowa Agricultural College he earned his bachelor's degree in 1894.
b. 14	7. At age 10 he left the plantation to find a school that would open its doors to him.
II. 8	8. George Washington Carver's years as a researcher at Tuskegee Institute in Alabama demonstrate his commitment to scientific exploration.
A. 5	
1. 11	9. As an adult, Carver worked to continue his studies in college.
2. 1	10. First, Carver enrolled at Simpson College in Indianola, Iowa where he studied piano and painting.
B. 2	11. His work at Tuskegee diversified southern agriculture so that it no longer depended on cotton.
	12. No local grade school was open to black children, but Carver applied himself and learned to read and write at home.
	13. Later, Carver transferred to Iowa Agricultural College (now ISU) becoming the first African American student to enroll.
	14. He also worked as a faculty member and researcher at Iowa Agricultural College while he completed his Master's degree from 1894-1896.

C - credibility
A - attention getter
R - reveal topic
R - relate to audience
P - preview

Starting off on the Wrong Foot: Flawed Introductions Exercise

Here are four complete introductions from classroom speeches. Each has at least one flaw that keeps it from working as well as it could to prepare the listeners for the speech to come. In each case, identify the parts of a good speech introduction [CARRP] that are missing or flawed and make specific suggestions for improving the introduction.

1.)   A   Can you imagine a creature with jaws strong enough to crush bones? What about a creature with fangs perfectly engineered for grabbing and ripping flesh? What if I told you that this creature lives in half of all homes in the United States?

R   Many of us have one or more canine companions or, at the very least, we know friends or families who have dogs. R

P   Today I'm going to discuss the reasons dogs bite, the warning signs to look for before a dog bites, and how to safely approach a dog.

Missing credibility, could improve the R's to connect better with the preview

2.)   Pizza, hamburgers, smoothies. If you drank water or ate food today then you will really be interested in my topic. As Iowans we are fairly secure in our supplies of food and water but, for a big part of the world's population, these things are already a problem. Today I'm going to tell you about the three biggest problems with population growth. *Attention getter poorly connected to topic. Poor topic revelation. No credibility. Why does this relate to us?*

3.)   How many people spend some time exercising 5 days a week? According to the American Heart Association, all adults under the age of 65 years are recommended to do at least 30 minutes of moderate-intensity exercise 5 days a week. *–A*

I've been taking fitness classes during the past four years through Recreation Services; my favorite class is Yoga. *–credibility*

Today I'm going to inform you about what a yoga practice involves, what benefits can be found in yoga, and urge you to go take yoga at one of the great places it is offered here in Ames. *–P*

Needs to relate it to the audience. Could use a clearer topic revelation

4.)   As citizens of Ames we rely on the strength of its local economy. We eat out, we buy groceries, we purchase textbooks and video games, we go to movies, see shows, and watch sporting events. All of this is possible because of the local economy. *–A/Relate*

I'm an economics major and have focused my personal research on the mechanics of local economies—how they thrive and survive. *–C*

It's a fact that chain restaurants send the majority of their profits from Ames to corporate headquarters somewhere else. This funneling of money weakens our local economy. I'm here to talk to you about the things we can do to stop this deadly process. *–Reveal*

Jumps to chain restaurants, needs a better connect. Lacks a preview

Using Visual Aids

Visual Aids offer an extra opportunity to communicate with your audience. The key word here is VISUAL! While sometimes a speaker uses words in a visual aid to help reinforce the ideas in the speech, many of today's most successful speakers integrate images and, occasionally, multimedia to help them present new information in an engaging way. In addition to traditional visuals such as PowerPoint and Overhead slides, don't forget about the advantages of using actual objects—such as when you show an audience a model airplane to help demonstrate how planes lift off the ground.

Though almost any visual aid is better than none in terms of audience interest, poor visual aids can distract an audience, create a barrier to clear communication and hurt your credibility. The following Dos and Don'ts can help you make good choices concerning visual aids. Chapter 13 has a detailed discussion. Specific information about the use of PowerPoint during presentations is in the following pages and in the appendix of your textbook. Talk to your lab instructor to get more information about specific issues concerning visual aid use in your classrooms.

DO: ☺	DON'T: ☹
Be prepared to use the visual aid. • bring all materials needed–conversion plug for your computer, tape, extra poster board for mounting or covering the visual aid, etc. Rehearse with the visual aid; know where you will place it, when you will reveal it, how you will refer to it. If using technology, practice revealing and hiding slides and practice hooking up the equipment. Work with others speaking the same day to coordinate who will bring equipment to limit the number of computer switches needed each day. Have a back-up plan when using technology. Show the visual aid as you are discussing it and spend time making sure the point it is illustrating is clear. It is a fine thing to move over to your visual to explain it. Be sure that the visual aid adds something useful to the presentation. Make the visual large enough for all to see. • Use at least 18-20 pt. font for overheads and PowerPoint slides • Leave empty space on the slides or overheads • Test visual aids in the room for visibility • Use models instead of tiny objects If needed, arrange before class to have someone from the class help you with your aid. Aim to have a visual that looks both professional and creative.	Ruin your credibility by letting the audience see that you are unprepared to use the visual aid. Give the speech without practicing with the visual aid. [It can take much longer to present the visual aid than you expect.] Expect someone to rescue you when technology fails. Substitute the visual aid for the speech (this is an especially tempting error when using multimedia. Say you can't give the speech if something goes wrong with the visual aid. Let the visual aid distract the audience (or you) from the content of the speech. Say "you can't see this but...." or use a visual aid too small to be seen with ease by all. Use an overhead or image made from an article or table right out of a book, magazine, newspaper, or off the Internet without enlarging it and cropping unneeded material. Make the visual aid visually cluttered. Pass a visual aid among the audience members in a formal or semi-formal setting. Look unprofessional. (Check your spelling!) Use only words on your visual; use images too. Use visuals only to meet an assignment requirement; they can add interest every time you speak.

Speaking With PowerPoint

The appendix to your textbook contains an excellent discussion about PowerPoint with advice about formatting slides and some general delivery guidelines. Here are a few additional tips to help you succeed.

1. Slide Development Tips

- PowerPoint adds the most to a presentation when it brings visuals, not text, to the audience. It is okay to have only images in a PowerPoint presentation.
- When using PowerPoint to present both text and visuals, aim to follow the 6 x 6 x 6 rule.
  - no more than 6 lines on a slide
  - no more than 6 words in each line
  - no more than 6 slides of text before you have an image
- Avoid paragraphs. Use short declarative sentences or phrases for bullets.
- Use "builds" and text animation rarely and when you do use them be consistent in order to indicate your structure.
- Limit use animated transitions from slide to slide; if you do use them, be consistent in order to reinforce the relationships between the points.
- **Use a spell checker and proofread your slides**.

Remember, slides are visual aids. They should support your presentation, not substitute for it.

2. PowerPoint Commands Useful when Delivering a Presentation

To advance one slide or to proceed through a series of builds on a slide

- Use the down ↓ arrow, right → arrow, space bar, the N key, page down, or even clicking the left mouse key.
- Mouse keys often make an audible click, so avoid using them especially for builds during the presentation. The exception is if you have a remote mouse that will let you advance slides away from the computer. In this case, use the remote mouse; the advantage of your freedom of movement outweighs any concern about a minor click.
- Whichever of the 6 options you choose, get used to one and apply it consistently

To step back one slide or to remove the most recent build on a slide

- Use the up ↑ arrow, left ← arrow, the P key, page up, or backspace
- Whichever of the 5 options you choose, get used to one and apply it consistently

To jump ahead or backward in the presentation by more than one slide

- Refer to your printout of the slides, find the number of the slide you want
- Using the number keys, put in the slide number and hit return
- This tool is useful for adapting to time constraints or for responding to questions from the audience.

To have a blank black screen at any point

- Hit the period key or the B key
- To bring back the screen you were before you hit the key, hit period or B again.
- This key stroke is very useful if you want to pause and have the complete attention of the audience for a moment, if you want to pause to take questions, or if you need to pause for a break or to adapt to some other interference

To have a blank white screen at any point

- Hit the W key
- To bring back the screen you were before you hit the key, hit W again.
- This key stroke is useful if you are in a very dark room, but want to pause and have the complete attention of the audience for a moment if you want to pause to take questions, or if you need to pause for a break or to adapt to some other interference

To draw attention to a particular point or feature of the slide—use "the pencil" to circle, underline or point to it.

- To enable this feature, while in presentation mode, click on the right mouse button and choose "Pointer Options" from the menu.

  - To have a tool simply to point at something, choose arrow
  - To be able to draw on the slide, choose pen, and then choose a pen color that will be visible on your slides

    - To activate the pen during the presentation, move the mouse around until the pen is where you wish to begin to underline or circle.
    - Press the left mouse button and move the pen to leave a colored line.

  - Used sparingly, this strategy can be useful in a lengthy presentation since it lets you change the look of the slide for the purposes of underscoring or emphasizing a particular point for that particular audience.

3. Considerations when Preparing to Use PowerPoint

General Advice:

- Avoid the automatic advance features of the system.
- Set up a PowerPoint remote or wireless mouse if it is available to you (but make sure it is properly installed and that you have extra batteries for the remote mouse).
- Rehearse the presentation with the technology; practicing advancing the slides and creating the builds is important for timing and muscle memory. You want your mind to be focused on your verbal message and on being responsive to the audience rather than on the mechanics of your visual aid.

- When you are in the "real world," be sure that your oral presentation adds value to the visuals. If it doesn't then, rethink your presentation strategy, what are the advantages to your sharing this information in person rather than through a written report? When you speak make sure the focus is on you!

Tips about the Speaking Environment:

- Avoid letting the audience sit in total, or even deep, darkness.
- Encourage audience members to sit closer together if they are scattered all around the room and there are many empty seats.
- Check the front of the room:
    - You will need a table on which to set up the equipment
    - Make sure you have an extension cord so that you need not rely on your batteries
    - If you want a lectern or podium for your notes, be sure it is available.
    - Be sure that you have some way of lighting your own notes.

4. Delivery Tips Especially for PowerPoint Presentations

Maintain eye contact with the audience

- Occasionally glance at, but do not read to the audience from, the screen behind you.
- Similarly, do not read from (or stare at) the computer screen in front of you.
- Prepare speaking notes which you can reference during the presentation, but do not read to the audience.
- Spread eye contact to all parts of the room so that each listener can feel that you care that they, as an individual, understand this information.

Use your voice to maximize impact.

- Beware of rushing through the presentation. The audience is absorbing information both orally and visually. They need time to take it all in.
- Be open to feedback from the audience suggesting a need to slow down, speed up, or to take a break.
- The goal is to speak to the audience conversationally.
    - Make sure that you use a good deal of variety in your speaking rate and in your inflection.
    - Make sure that you use pauses and that these are silent rather than filled with "um" or "and." This will help give the audience time to take in the message.
    - Your voice must help to signal what is the MOST IMPORTANT information.

49

Use your body effectively to help enliven the message.

- Avoid staying right next to the computer during the entire presentation.

    - When there is a slide that will require more than a minute of speaking time, feel free to move away from the computer and toward the other parts of your audience.
    - A moment of silence is okay if you need to go back to your computer to advance to the next screen.

- If you are on a stage and must stay near the computer, be sure that your face and upper body gestures are at times quite dynamic so that you can re-engage listeners through physical delivery.

Sample Informative Speeches
Questions for Analysis

As you read sample speeches in the textbook, view sample speeches in lecture, or listen to speeches in lab, practice paying attention to the choices speakers make as they aim to inform. Be sure to ask yourself questions such as these.

1. What are the main points of the speech? State them in the form you might use for a formal outline.

2. Find examples of the various types of connectives discussed in class in the sample speech. Why are connectives so important for informative speakers?

3. What kinds of supporting materials are used to develop the speech? Are sources for all of the materials clearly cited?

4. What special steps did the speaker take to use materials and language aimed to engage the audience?

5. What special steps did the speaker take to use delivery to build credibility, engage you as a listener and help you understand the topic?

6. How well are all of the functions of an Introduction and Conclusion accomplished in this speech? Point out the best and the weakest features of the Intro and Conclusion.

Preparation Outline Checklist for the Informative Speech Outline

Use this checklist as a guide to examining preparation outlines. These are the same criteria your instructor will use to grade your outline.

Specific Purpose and Central Idea Statements [2 pt.] • Are they stated at the top of the outline? • Do they follow the guidelines in the textbook?	
Pattern of Organization [2 pt.] • Is the pattern of organization correctly identified? (Look at the Roman Numerals, do they follow that pattern?)	
Introduction [2 pt.] • CARRP: are all 5 parts included? • Are all parts labeled accurately?	
Main Points [4 pts.] • Are points stated in single complete sentences? • Are symbols used properly? • Are the main points separate and distinct? Is parallel wording used when possible? • Are the main points in body developed in the same order as was promised by the Preview Statement?	
Sub-points [4 pts.] • Are sub-points stated in single complete sentences? • Are symbols used properly and the rule of division followed? (if there is an A there is a B, if there is a 1 there is a 2) • Do the sub-points clearly fit under the main point as it is stated? • Is the speaker making sense of information for us? (language clear; pts. are not cut and pasted from sources)	
Connectives [2 pt.] • Are the connectives included before and between each of the main points? • Are connectives identified and properly labeled?	
Conclusion [2pt.] • Does the conclusion Signal the End and Reinforce the Central Idea? • Are the parts properly labeled?	
Sources / Bibliography [2 pt.] • Are sources noted in the body of the outline as well as the bibliography? • Does the citation in the bibliography provide enough information to locate the source?	

Strategies for Reducing Speech Anxiety

When Preparing for Your Presentation

< Pay special attention to preparing and rehearsing the introduction.
< Wear clothing that is both comfortable and that helps you to feel at your best.
< Investigate the room before the speech. Visualize your speech in that room. See yourself giving the speech successfully to a warm and interested audience.
< Rehearse the speech with an outline and then with just a few notes; don't try to say the same words every time; focus on the ideas you want to share.
< Plan to use visual aids that will let you move during the speech.
< Rehearse some body movement–gestures or steps so that you can release nervous energy in a positive way.
< Use positive self-talk.
< If nervous energy tends to sneak up on you during speeches then get rid of some of that energy before you enter the room where you will speak: go up and down some stairs or do some jumping jacks.
< Take a few deep breaths and picture the stress leaving your body as you exhale.

During Your Presentation

< Walk to the front of the room with confidence; it may not feel like real confidence yet, but you know what it looks like and can aim to walk and stand in a way that suggests confidence.
< Look at the audience in a friendly way before beginning to speak and take a couple of good breaths.
< Don't rush the introduction. Be willing to diverge from your prepared text to make an impromptu comment that can help you bond with the audience (for example, you might connect your speech with a previous presentation).
< Let yourself notice audience members who smile or nod their head. Focus on your success in communicating with them clearly.
< Do not apologize ahead of time for any errors or for being nervous (they want to hear what you came to share with them; don't invite them to worry about you).
< Adopt behaviors that appear relaxed and comfortable (a reasonable pace, a smile, a comfortable pause, a nice gesture, an off-hand remark, eye contact spread around the room, good vocal variation).
< Engage the audience rather than trying to hide from them.

After Your Presentation

< Give yourself credit and accept compliments graciously.
< Learn from any mistakes, but don't beat yourself up. There is no perfect speech. Focus as much on what you did well as you do on what you hope to do better next time.
< Ask for feedback on your presentation. Though it is nice to hear compliments, we learn from hearing about things that could have gone better, so ask questions that can facilitate your learning.

Unit II: Persuasive Speaking

The Persuasive Speech of Policy Assignment

Purpose and Topic:

The purpose of this assignment is to develop a message designed to persuade the audience for or against a question of policy. Speeches on questions of policy deal with specific problems and typically argue that a particular course of action should be adopted to solve those problems. Once again it may be possible to select a topic that is controversial in your chosen area of study. An education major may want to examine policies about year-around schooling, an agriculture major may weigh-in on policies concerning hog lots or pesticides, while a business major may wish to pursue a case concerning the capital gains tax or protective tariffs.

Assignment and Process:

Once you have chosen a topic you will develop a specific purpose statement following the format: "To persuade my audience that <u>We</u> <u>should</u> do Y." Your goal is to persuade your class that some group "we" belong to—each of us as individuals, this class, the ISU community, the Ames community, Central Iowa, Iowa or even "We" as the People of the United States who might act through Congress, or "we" as members of the United Nations—should take a particular action to solve, or take a step toward solving, a particular problem. One big challenge is to engage this particular audience, so you have to be clear about what their role is in the situation. Once you have a topic, you will then analyze the PROBLEM (Need), PLAN, and PRACTICALITY issues for your subject. When you have decided on the issues and claims you need to prove to convince the audience of your position you will need to gather the necessary research materials. The campus and public libraries, organizations interested in this issue, and individuals knowledgeable about the subject are all good sources for you to investigate. In addition to gathering evidence and creating arguments to prove your case, you will want to attend to both credibility and emotional issues. People often need to be appealed to on these levels if they are to act on the things you have convinced them of through evidence and reasoning.

As you do your research you will also be creating a central idea and developing ideas about which organizational structure will best suit your case. Chapter 15 discusses some new patterns of organization particularly suited to the persuasive speech. Chapter 16 discusses ways to argue and prove your points persuasively.

Requirements:

The following are the specific requirements of this assignment; the feedback page offers details about the factors of the actual speech assessment.

1) The time limit for the speech is 8 minutes. Make sure you choose a topic you can deal with in this amount of time. The full minute window on either side of the 8 minute limit gives you plenty of time to add an aside or restate a point as needed while you speak. Failure to meet

the time limit will result in a 1/3 letter grade penalty that will increase at 30 second intervals [so the first penalties begin at 6:59 and 9:01, the next 1/3 deduction is added at 6:29 and at 9:30, etc.]

2) Topic choices must be approved by your lab instructor. Topic choices must be submitted online through the SpCm 212 Blackboard site. Some instructors will have special requirements concerning the focus on your topic for your lab section, so be sure to follow their direction about topic selection. Be sure to check for your feedback.

3) Clearly use one of the patterns of organization discussed in the text and in class: Problem-Solution, Problem-Cause-Solution, Monroe's Motivated Sequence, or Comparative Advantages.

4) Use of at least <u>four</u> strong sources is required. We expect college level sources—use the tools that you learned about in Library 160 or in your English classes; not just Google searches (see "Source Requirements and Citing Sources for the Persuasive Speeches" below). These sources, be they books, articles, or individuals, must be cited orally during the speech and included in a bibliography at the end of your outline. Failure to cite sources orally will result in a 1/3 letter grade penalty for each source left out, such that a speech without source citations would be graded down over a full letter grade. Failure to cite sources properly orally or in the bibliography or choosing to cut and paste together an outline (even with citations) may result in a plagiarism or academic dishonest inquiry (for citation help, see "Sample Source Citation Guide for Bibliographies" above).

5) Delivery of the speech is to be extemporaneous--from no more than five (one-sided) note cards. Give the speech from a brief speaking outline, <u>not</u> from memory, manuscript, or full sentence outline. Failure to deliver the speech from a speaking outline will have an impact on the success of the speech (and so, on your grade).

6) Meet the Visual Aid requirement as explained by your lab instructor.

7) Two copies of typed complete drafts of your outline are due by the workshop day indicated on the syllabus.

8) A typed final preparation outline, including a full bibliography, is due at the beginning of your lab section on your assigned speaking day. Final outline **must also be uploaded to the Blackboard site** by the end of you speaking day.

In addition to meeting these requirements, the major grading criteria for this speech are: structure, clarity, full and interesting development of ideas, strength of analysis (Problem, Plan and Practicality), strength of reasoning and evidence, relating to/adapting to/involving and responding to the concerns of the audience, and delivery skills. See the feedback form for more details.

Persuasive Speech Feedback Form

Speaker _____

Topic _____

Guide: O-outstanding S-satisfactory N–needs work

1.	Gained attention	O S N	***INTRODUCTION***
2.	Topic clear	O S N	
3.	Related to audience	O S N	
4.	Credibility and goodwill established	O S N	
5.	Body previewed	O S N	
6.	Main points clear	O S N	***BODY***
7.	Pattern of organization used appropriately	O S N	
8.	Language clear, vivid	O S N	
9.	Connectives effective	O S N	
10.	Maintained eye contact	O S N	***DELIVERY***
11.	Voice effective	O S N	
12.	Facial expressiveness strong	O S N	
13.	Delivery stance strong	O S N	
14.	Gestures helpful	O S N	
15.	Visual aids presented well	O S N	
16.	Problem issue convincing	O S N	***ARGUMENT***
17.	Plan clearly explained	O S N	
18.	Practicality demonstrated	O S N	
19.	Sufficient evidence	O S N	
20.	Qualified sources of evidence	O S N	
21.	Ethos, Logos & Pathos all used	O S N	
22.	Addresses the Opposition	O S N	
23.	Prepared audience for ending	O S N	***CONCLUSION***
24.	Reinforced central idea	O S N	
25.	Topic challenging	O S N	***OVERALL***
26.	Presentation of self strong	O S N	
27.	Speech adapted to audience	O S N	
28.	Speech met the assignment	O S N	

Closing Comments:

Constructing the Case for the Defense of the Status Quo:
Or, "My Topic Doesn't Fit the Assignment!"

Sometimes you have to change topics to fit the demands of the situation (or the assignment), but if what you want to do can be construed as a defense of the *status quo* rather than a call for a change, you may still be able to pursue it. Most of the material in the book and in lecture, however, focuses on how to argue for change. You will need to talk to your TA about your speech as a special case to see if it can meet the assignment requirements. Here is a quick look at how such cases are built using class vocabulary.

Step One: Analyze your Topic

If your topic meets the following requirements, feel free to discuss it with your lab instructor.

1. The topic concerns a policy issue—it is focused on whether some action should or should not be taken.
2. The topic is one that the audience has heard about and it is safe to assume that they know some of the arguments that those arguing for change have voiced.
3. There is adequate support material available to build a defensive case.

For example, take the discussion of the speed limit on freeways in Iowa. Many states, including Iowa, have increased speed limits in the past few years, but after looking at accident data and gasoline use some people are advocating a return to the 65 m.p.h. speed limit. This is the kind of issue where one could now present a speech supporting keeping a change back to 65 miles per hour from the present 70 limit, <u>or</u> one could argue against such a change. Both cases need to be made well in order for the community to make a wise decision.

Step Two: Consider these strategies for organizing your case.

1. There is still a need to address the **Problem, Plan and Practicality** issues, but your approach is quite different.

    a. In a sense, the **Problem** issue is that someone is trying to change a perfectly good system. You'll want to make that clear <u>in the introduction</u> since that is the context of your case. Five years ago there was no need to argue that the speed limit should remain 65, but now there is a need to defend the speed limit.

    b. Your **Plan** would be whatever you want the audience or community to do to protect the *status quo*. Often you can say this in the introduction, though there are cases where the call to action could wait until the conclusion of the speech.

    c. Often the bulk of the body of the speech deals with **Practicality**, for it is here that you show that the present system works well and that the change proposed by your opponents would cause more harm than good.

2. Sometimes a topical pattern of organization can work best for this type of persuasive speech.

a. Here is an example of a set of main points in a topical pattern of organization:

I. The 70 mph highway speed limit should remain in effect because it saves time.
II. The 70 mph highway speed limit should remain in effect because it saves money.
III. The 70 mph highway speed limit should remain in effect because it does not create serious harms to the people of Iowa.

b. As you can see, the first two points deal with reasons why the present system is a good idea. The last main point is an effort to respond to the arguments presented by those who want change. It is an effort to refute the claims of those who say that the 70 mph limit hurts Iowans by increasing deaths and injuries. The speaker must counter this claim because it is the major argument of those supporting a change.

c. In a topical pattern, then, some of your main points will give reasons that support the present system and some of your points will focus on refuting the arguments and evidence of those calling for change.

3. Sometimes a Comparative Advantages structure will work best for a speech that is defending the *status quo*.

a. Here is an example of what the main points might look like in a Comparative Advantages case:

I. A higher speed limit is better than a lower speed limit because it saves money for enforcement and fosters public respect for law enforcement.
II. A higher speed limit is better than a lower speed limit because it is more energy efficient.
III. A higher speed limit is better than a lower speed limit because business gains in terms of time and efficiency outweigh the small increase in safety concerns.

b. Note how in the Comparative Advantage case each point raises a specific comparison and contrast between the two competing Plans.

So, it is possible to make an argument in defense of the *status quo* fit this assignment, but you still need to use the **Problem, Plan and Practicality** system when analyzing the topic and make sure each of the three is addressed in the speech. **Practicality**, however, will require the greatest amount of attention.

Sample Specific Purpose Statements for Persuasive Speeches of Policy
Just to give you an idea about some speech topic students have developed during the past few semesters.

To persuade my audience that the Iowa Board of Education should institute a year around school calendar.

To persuade my audience to sign a pledge to never use a hand-held cell phone while driving.

To persuade my audience that the FCC should pass new rules to restrict language use on the airwaves.

To persuade my audience to take action to demand increased Federal support for America's National Parks system.

To persuade my audience that Iowa schools should not sell soda or junk food in vending machines located in the schools.

To persuade my audience that the state of Iowa should enforced tougher penalties for the ban on texting while driving.

To persuade my audience that they should save and donate pop tabs to the Ronald McDonald House Charity.

To persuade my audience that states should pass the National Popular Vote bill in order to eliminate the current Electoral College system.

To persuade my audience to eat vegetarian at least one day a week.

To persuade my audience that the Veteran's Administration should revise its health plans to increase support for women veterans.

To persuade my audience that restaurants should decrease their portion sizes to meet the recommended nutritional standards.

To persuade my audience that the state of Iowa should increase penalties for driving while under the influence.

To persuade my audience that the state of Iowa should legalize medical marijuana.

To persuade my audience that NASA should continue to have manned missions into space.

Source Requirements and Citing Sources for the Persuasive Speeches

1. The Persuasive speech requires a minimum of 4 good sources. How do you know if you are using good sources? The textbook discussion in chapters 6 and 7 offer much guidance. Remember that in addition to the fundamental question—Will this help me prove a claim to establish the Problem or the Practicality or to help explain my Plan?—there are four central questions to ask about your sources.

    Question #1: **Expertise?** Does the person who wrote this know what he/she is talking about?
    Question #2: **Bias?** Does the person who wrote this have financial or ideological interests which significantly distort his/her judgment?
    Question #3: **Reviewed?** Did anyone else spend time figuring out if this was good information?
    Question #4: **Recency?** Is the source up to date given the topic?

    In addition to the general principles governing good use of supporting material, the following guidelines cover how we count sources in this course.

2. Speeches must be supported with documentation from reputable sources. These sources of your support material <u>must</u> <u>be</u> <u>identified</u> <u>out</u> <u>loud</u> during your speech. For example:

    "The <u>New</u> <u>York</u> <u>State</u> <u>Journal</u> of <u>Medicine</u> describes a 2009 study in New York City designed to determine if data on the family history of cancer patients were being recorded by hospitals. They found that only four of sixty-four hospitals indicated familial recurrence of cancer on medical charts, and no hospital accrediting agency required that this information be recorded." (See below for more examples of oral citations of sources.)

3. Magazines, newspapers, books, pamphlets (from legitimate, respected, organizations), journals or interviews (only one interview "counts" per speech), may all be used as sources. But remember that listeners are much more critical of sources used in building arguments than they are about sources for informative speeches. Many excellent, reviewed and low-biased sources can now be accessed through the Web. In this course we distinguish between simple web sites (those accessible through search engines like Google which can have very weak credibility) and Internet access to material that has been reviewed by people in the field (strong credibility). Often these are web sites that contain material also available in published resources, such as http://jama.ama-assn.org which gives you access to the highly-respected <u>Journal</u> of <u>the</u> <u>American</u> <u>Medical</u> <u>Association</u> on-line. Use the web accessible materials available through the Iowa State Library's Instruction Library Guides; you can get there through our Blackboard site for SpCm 212 or through the library homepage [click on Classes & Tours Instruction LibGuides].

4. What counts? All of your citations for the speech cannot come from the same type of source, i.e. all magazines, all books, all newspapers or all web sites. And Dictionaries, general encyclopedias (including Britannica and Wikipedia), while helpful in providing background information, <u>will</u> <u>not</u> count as sources for the speeches.

5. Judging the quality of the sources in terms of how well it fits the claim you are trying to prove is important. Weak source material—web sites prepared by unknown people, or prepared by

elementary teachers for use by third graders, or entertainment media (movies, TV, humor columns in newspapers) should not be used as a source for facts. Neither should sources like the ISU Daily be used for national and international issues. To do so can hurt your credibility and so reduce the impact of your speech. See the "evaluating websites" tab on the 212 Instruction Library Guide page or chapter 6 in the textbook for advice about searching for and evaluating Internet resources.

6.   In addition to citing the sources orally in your speeches, you must include a bibliography of all sources used at the end of your preparation outline. For example:

- Hutchinson, Sue. "Some Chick Lit Provides More Than Empty Calories." *Mercury News* 24 May 2006. 29 May 2006 <http://web116.epnet.com/citation.asp?>.
- Will, George F. "Electronic Morphine." Newsweek 25 Nov. 2002: 92.

Use the "Sample Source Citation Guide" in this workbook (see the table of contents) for more examples of citations. The ConnectLucas website that accompanies your textbook also has detailed information for using either the APA style or MLA styles of citations.

7.   **The bottom line**: Failure to **orally cite** at least the minimum number of sources for the speech assignment will lead to grade deductions for the speech. Use of sources without oral citations or with improper bibliographic citation is a problem. Improper use of sources—simple cutting and pasting together the prose of others with or without minor changes—even with citation of some sort, can still go against the expectation that speakers work with materials & develop expertise before speaking, can hurt your grades or lead to plagiarism or academic dishonesty discussions.

Examples: In **persuasive speeches** the audience needs assurance that you have done diligent research and that the sources you are using are credible so the oral citations require more detail than citations for informative speeches. You should also identify the credentials of the source. Note that the supporting material can be quoted or paraphrased and that the source material is clearly linked to a point, a claim, which the speaker wants to prove.

- "In its recently updated online Health Fraud Kit, the FDA warns us to watch out for claims of FDA approval. They note, 'Current law does not permit the mention of 'FDA' or 'U.S. Food and Drug Administration' in any way that suggests marketing approval' for any medical drug or treatment.'"
- "Michael Fisher, Executive Director of the Sierra Club, claimed in an essay posted on the Sierra Club website, that unsafe disposal of alkali batteries will become one of America's most serious environmental threats during the next three to five years."
- "The Boston Globe warned on March 19, 2001, that mercury, lead, and cadmium can enter our respiratory system through the air we breathe or through contaminated food and/or water."
- [*In persuasive speeches even examples should have a citation*] "Ruth Conrad's story, from the October 2008 issue of Redbook magazine, is only one in a string of thousands. Consumer's Research in February 2009, estimated that American's spent $27 billion on fraudulent health care products that year, with one out of every four Americans falling victim to health fraud."

Research Tips for the Persuasive Speech

1. Don't start with Google; instead begin your search with the materials and links provided in the ISU Library's Class Guide for SpCm 212.

- You can get there through the our Blackboard site or http://instr.iastate.libguides.com/spcm212
- After you have examined that material, click on "Resources" in the tab along the top. Especially helpful under this tab is the AcademicSearch Elite and the Ebsco databases which will take you to resources available in both popular magazines as well as the better known research journals. Also there is the LexisNexis Academic link for newspaper resources. All of these indexes will take you directly to many full text articles; all of these sources are reviewed so the quality of the information is better than you would likely get with an open Google search [Note: to access these resources from off campus, you will need your student I.D. and library PIN numbers.]

2. When conducting electronic searches try a few different variations on your subject terms.

3. If you are having trouble locating articles:
- use the help function of the database
- talk to the reference librarians

4. Keep track of the resources you uncover for your bibliography and so you can find them again as needed. Write them down. Cut and paste info and citations into a WORD document. Print them out. E-mail them to yourself. Just be sure to keep a record.
- As you record citations, be sure that you have all of the information needed to fulfill the requirements of MLA or APA bibliographic form. Author(s) (or sponsoring organization for Web Sites), title(s), publishing information (where and by whom), date of publication (and volume number in some cases), and page numbers. For web sites you will also want to note the URL, the date of last update of the source and the date you accessed that source at that URL.
- **Sample web site citation:** *Key Facts about Mumps.* 14 April 2006. Center for Disease Control. 24 May 2006 <http://www.cdc.gov/nip/diseases/mumps/vac-chart.htm>. [See the Sample Source Citation Guide for more examples.]

5. Don't overlook the usefulness of books as a resource for your persuasive speeches. Even if the book you are looking for is not on the shelf, the other books in that area of the library are likely to help you. You don't need to read an entire book in order to use parts of it in your speech. Use the index in the back of the book to help you locate materials useful to your case.

6. As you locate support materials, note whether they are useful for the Problem, Plan, or Practicality sections of your argument. Find a variety of support materials—statistics, examples, and testimony—for each major part of the speech so that you can build your logos, pathos and ethos.

7. Don't rely on Wikipedia or any other encyclopedia as anything more than a starting point for your research; use high quality sources that give you strong Examples, Statistics and Testimony.

Sample Persuasive Speech of Policy: Manuscript

Darfur
By Brian Burmeister

1. Genocide. For many of us the word implies *history*: World War II, the Nazis, and their campaign against the Jewish people. It implies a time and a world from which we are now over 60 years removed. For such a thing could only happen in the distant past. It certainly couldn't happen in our world. Not today. Not in the year 2010.

2. But it is happening. As I speak, genocide is happening in the African country of Sudan, in its western region called Darfur—and it's been happening there for over seven years. The African people there have been systematically forced from their homes by the Arab government that runs the country, and without proper means to protect themselves they have been murdered—mercilessly slaughtered by the hundreds of thousands—by the order of their own government.

3. As human beings, we have a choice: we can turn a blind eye and say that genocide is not our problem, or we can take a stand, and as a society can save thousands, possibly even millions of lives.

4. For over three years now, I have been active in this cause. I have served as President of Ames-ISU for Darfur, a student organization whose mission is to help educate ISU's student body and the general public of Ames regarding the crisis in Darfur. Because of what I have learned while studying these issues the past three years, I have also written letters to our Senators Tom Harkin and Chuck Grassley, urging legislation that would help the people suffering there, and I have written letters to the editors of various newspapers including the <u>Des Moines Register</u>, begging the people of Iowa, like all of you, to contribute to charities such as the World Food Programme, which do so much to supply the people of Darfur with the keys to life, such as daily food.

5. Today I will share with you the tragic size and scope of the crisis in Darfur, and then I will share a solution that takes an important step toward alleviating the suffering. To begin, the crisis in Darfur has three horrifying and unforgiveable elements to it: displacement, rape, and death.

6. The first horror of Darfur is displacement. At its most basic level, the situation in Darfur is this, that you have a government—the Sudanese government—which represents a minority of the country's population and who feels their power threatened by the majority population of the country. Brian Steidle, a former U.S. marine and U.S. representative to the African Union observer mission in Darfur, spent six months in Darfur investigating what was unfolding there. In his book, *The Devil Came on Horseback*, he shared his assessment of the origins of this practice of displacement: "An initial uprising among black African tribes seeking greater rights had been quickly squelched by the oppressive, Arab-led Government of Sudan. The government took the occasion to dig deeper trenches between the African farming villages and the Arab nomadic herders of Darfur. By arming Arab nomads, the Government of Sudan had orchestrated a bloody campaign of terror to wipe out the black ethnic groups and permanently alter the demography of the region." What happened was, the Government of Sudan trained and armed the Janjaweed, a militia whose name literally translates to devils on horseback. As Steidle goes on to explain in his book, "The more I learned about the Janjaweed, the more I saw them as the government's loyal attack dog." As you can see from these pictures in Steidle's book, which he took himself, the Janjaweed burn every home in every town and village they come across, so that there are no homes for those who were lucky enough to survive the attacks to return to.

7. These attacks have happened on such a large scale that The Internal Displacement Monitoring Centre, an international body who monitors displacement resulting from conflict, states that there are at least 4.9 million displaced persons in the country of Sudan, with at least 2.7 million of that total being concentrated within its Darfur region.

8. To complicate matters even more, the BBC News reports that almost all of those 2.7 million people live in displaced persons camps as a result. Within these camps, people must rely on outside sources of food being brought in order to survive.

9. Unlike us, those living within the displaced persons camps don't have electric stoves or microwaves to prepare their food. They are largely dependent on firewood to cook, and as Darfur is largely desert, this means that travel of up to several miles is sometimes required to obtain the necessary wood.

10. This leads directly into the second horror of Darfur: rape. Within the camps, it is the responsibility of women and girls to obtain the necessary firewood. The Janjaweed

know this, and so they wait for small groups of women to leave the protection of their camps before they make their attack.

11. Pamela Shifman, a UN expert on sexual violence, who visited the region, told the UN News Service that every single woman and girl she spoke to within the displaced persons camps had either been sexually assaulted by the Janjaweed or knew of a woman or girl who had been.

12. To make matters worse, according to a CNN report, when women report rapes to the police, the police don't write anything down, they don't ask questions, and they don't even ask the victims for their names.

13. A December 10, 2006 press release from the Save Darfur Coalition which shared words from one female survivor of the tragedy in Darfur, shows that that is not the worst the police will do. This woman bravely said, "Janjaweed militia and Government soldiers attacked a primary school for girls, raping the pupils. . . . Because I told people what happened, the authorities arrested me. They said, 'We will show you what rape is.' They beat me severely. At night, three men raped me. The following day the same thing, different men. Torture and rape, every day, torture and rape."

14. With all the tragedy that is befalling the women, I'm sure you are asking yourself, "Well, why, with all these terrible things happening, aren't the men going out for the firewood?" And the answer to this is as horrible as it is obvious: because the men would be killed.

15. The third horror of Darfur is death. According to Dr. Salah Hassan, Director of Africana Studies and Research Center at Cornell University, estimates based upon figures from the World Health Organization, the United Nations, and the Center for International Justice placed the loss of life in Darfur somewhere "between 280,000 and 310,000" as of the beginning of 2005. Since 2006, the United Nations estimates that 300,000 more casualties have been claimed in the crisis. The loss of life in Darfur is simply unimaginable.

16. So far we have seen the horrible tragedies which are occurring in Darfur. And I'm sure you're asking yourself, as I've asked myself many times, "What can I do?" The answer to this is a lot, and it only takes a little.

17. Ten dollars.

18. By contributing $10 to Ames-ISU for Darfur's t-shirt fundraiser, not only will you be getting yourself a t-shirt, but far more important, you will be supporting either the Solar Cooker Project or the World Food Programme. The shirts were generously donated to our group in order to help get out the word about Darfur; since there is no cost to us for the shirt, your full $10 goes directly to these projects.

19. Supporting the Solar Cooker Project reduces the possibility of rape for women and girls living within the displaced persons camps. Jewish World Watch, a humanitarian organization concerned with genocide, as well the group implementing the Solar Cooker Project, reports that within the camps in which solar-powered stoves have been fully distributed, women and girls are now making 86% fewer trips away from the camps than they were before the solar-powered stoves were used. Think about that. 86% fewer trips away from the camps means an 86% decrease in the chance that women and girls will be raped by the Janjaweed.

20. Every $30 donated to the Project is enough to purchase and distribute two solar-powered stoves—which is enough to last one family in Darfur for an entire year. So if you, along with the person to your left, and the person to your right, were all to donate $10 to the cause, the three of you would have a very real impact on the lives of an entire family in Darfur.

21. But as we learned earlier, rape is not the only tragedy in Darfur. Supporting the World Food Programme helps sustain life for those living within the displaced persons camps. The World Food Programme provides monthly food rations to an estimated 2 million displaced persons in Darfur. That's 2 million people, completely dependent on the support of others, every single day. The United Nations estimates that without proper resources, as many as 100,000 people could die within the displaced persons camps due to starvation every single month.

22. $10 is not difficult to give. For most of us, $10 could easily be saved by simply choosing to eat at home twice in the near future, instead of eating those same two meals in a restaurant. So I'm not asking you to sacrifice anything, certainly not food, just how you get that food.

23. We may not be able to do anything to change the whole political landscape of the Sudan and fix the underlying causes of these problems, but we can take this small step to alleviate the worst of the consequences. Last year, students like you helped the Ames-ISU for Darfur group send $1500 to these programs.

24. As we have seen, the ongoing crisis in Darfur is unimaginable: nearly 3 million people have been forced from their homes, countless rapes have occurred, and more than half a million lives have been lost in the conflict.

25. But we have also seen that there is hope, that there are things each and every one of us can do, and that such efforts can have very real, very positive impacts on the people living there.

26. A man far smarter than myself once said, "Don't tell me what you value. Show me your budget and I'll show you what you value."

27. And I would like to think that in the days and weeks ahead, everyone of you can honestly show yourselves that you value protecting someone's mother, someone's sister, someone's daughter from the possibility of rape, or supplying someone with a meal who might not otherwise have one, far more than you value another trip to McDonald's.

SAMPLE PROBLEM-SOLUTION
PERSUASIVE SPEECH OF POLICY: OUTLINE

Here is the same speech on Darfur as it was turned in as a final outline for the persuasive speech of policy. Note the similarities and differences between the manuscript and the outline.

Brian Burmeister, Fall 2009
Lab Section 22
Lab Instructor: Justin Atwell

Specific Purpose: To persuade my audience to donate $10 to the Solar Cooker Project and/or the World Food Programme through Ames-ISU for Darfur's "Save Darfur" t-shirt fundraiser.

Central Idea: The crisis in Darfur in tragic, but the suffering there can be reduced through the implementation of solar-powered stoves and supplies of food rations.

Pattern of Organization: Problem-Solution

Introduction:
   I.   **Attention (Arousing curiosity):** Genocide. For many of us the word implies *history*: World War II, the Nazis, and their campaign against the Jewish people. It implies a time and a world for which we are now over 60 years removed. For such a thing could only happen in the distant past. It certainly couldn't happen in our world. Not today. Not in the year 2010.
   II. **Reveal topic:** But it is happening. As I speak, genocide is happening in the African country of Sudan, in its western region called Darfur—and it's been happening there for over seven years. The African people there have been systematically forced from their homes by the Arab government that runs the country, and without proper means to protect themselves they have been murdered—mercilessly slaughtered by the hundreds of thousands—by the order of their own government.
   III. **Relate to the Audience:** As human beings, we have a choice: we can turn a blind eye and say that genocide is not our problem, or we can take a stand, and as a society can save thousands, possibly even millions of lives.
   IV. **Credibility (Personal):** For over three years now, I have been active in this cause. I have served as President of Ames-ISU for Darfur, a student organization whose mission is to help educate ISU's student body and the general public of Ames regarding the crisis in Darfur. **(Expert)** Because of what I have learned while studying these issues the past three years, I have also written letters to our Senators Tom Harkin and

Chuck Grassley, urging legislation that would help the people suffering there, and I have written letters to the editors of various newspapers including the <u>Des Moines Register</u>, begging the people of Iowa to contribute to charities such as the World Food Program, which do so much to supply the people of Darfur with the keys to life, such as daily food.

V. **Preview:** Today I will share with you the tragic size and scope of the crisis in Darfur, and then I will share a solution that takes an important step toward alleviating the suffering.

Body:

Connective (Internal preview): To begin, the crisis in Darfur has three horrifying elements: displacement, rape, and death.

I. The tragedy of Darfur has created a serious human rights crisis.

    A. The first horror of Darfur is displacement.

> Including the source citation on the outline helps make sure you remember to cite it when you speak.

        1. The Sudanese government represents a minority of the population, feels threatened by the majority population and is using violence to change the demographics of the region.
            a. Former U.S. Marine and representative to African Union observer mission in Darfur, Brian Steidle, documents this history in his book, *The Devil Came on Horseback*.
            a. The government's initial response to an uprising grew to a reign of terror.
            b. The government has funded the Janjaweed, a militia who name translates to "devils on horseback."

        2. The Internal Displacement Monitoring Centre, an international body who monitors displacement, states there are at least 4.9 million displaced persons in the country of Sudan, with at least 2.7 million concentrated in the Darfur region.

        3. According to BBC News, almost all of those 2.7 million people live in displaced persons camps as a result.
            a. the people in the camps have no homes to go back to—the Janjaweed have razed their villages and homes.
            b. People within the camps rely on outside sources of food being brought in to survive.

     c. People depend on firewood to cook, but that requires travel outside the camps to collect wood.

Connective (Transition): This need to collect wood leads directly to the second horror of Darfur: rape.

B. The second horror of Darfur is rape.

> The use of parallel wording of A, B and C helps add clarity to the analysis of the Problem.

1. Women and girls are raped as a tool of terror when they leave the camps to get firewood.
    a. Pamela Shifman, a U.N. expert on sexual violence who visited the camps in Darfur, reported that every woman and girl she spoke to had either been sexually assaulted or personally knew of someone who had been.
    b. A December 10, 2006 press release from the Save Darfur Coalition shared words from one female survivor of the tragedy in Darfur.
2. CNN's report, "The War Crime of Rape in Darfur," said that when women report rape to the police, the police don't write anything down, don't ask questions, and don't even ask the victims for their names.

Connective (Transition): With all the tragedy that is befalling the women, you might ask, "Well, why then, with all these terrible things happening, aren't the men retrieving the firewood?" And the answer to this is as horrible as it is obvious: because the men would be killed.

> In A, B, and C we see balanced use of statistics to build logos, examples to build pathos and testimony to build ethos.

C. The third horror of Darfur is death.

1. According to Dr. Salah Hassan, Director of Africana Studies and Research Center at Cornell University, estimates from the World Health Organization, the United Nations, and the Center for International Justice place the loss of life in Darfur "between 280,000 and 310,000 at the beginning of 2005."
2. The United Nations estimates that 300,000 more casualties since 2006.

Connective (Transition): So far we have seen the horrible tragedies which are occurring in Darfur. And I'm sure you're asking yourself, as I've asked myself many times, "What can I do?" The answer to this is a lot, and it only takes a little.

II. You can help respond to this human rights crisis, by contributing $10 to Ames-ISU for Darfur's t-shirt fundraiser which supports the Solar Cooker Project and the World Food Programme.

A. Supporting the Solar Cooker Project reduces the possibility of rape for women and girls living within the displaced persons camps.

> The evidence here directly addresses the issue of **Practicality** by showing that this plan can work to reduce rape by reducing the need to leave the camps to collect wood.

    1. Jewish World Watch, implementer of the Solar Cooker Project, reports that within the camps where solar-powered stoves have been fully distributed, women and girls make 86% fewer trips away from the camps than before.

    2. Every $30 donated to the Project can purchase and distribute two solar-powered stoves which will last one family in Darfur an entire year.

Connective (Transition): But as we learned earlier, rape is not the only tragedy in Darfur. Food is also a problem.

B. Supporting the World Food Programme helps sustain life for those living within the displaced persons camps.

    1. The World Food Programme provides monthly food rations to an estimated 2 million displaced persons in Darfur.

    2. Without such programs, the U.N. estimates as many as 100,000 people could die due to starvation every single month.

> Having proven that the Plan is practical since it will help address the problems, here the speaker addresses Practicality by proving that it is not hard to adopt the plan.

C. $10 is not difficult to give.

    1. For most of us, $10 could easily be saved by simply by choosing to eat at home twice in the near future, instead of eating those same two meals in a restaurant.

    2. So I'm not asking you to sacrifice anything, certainly not food, just how you get that food.

D. We may not be able to change the political landscape of the Sudan, but Ames-ISU for Darfur sent $1500 last year to help improve people's lives.

Conclusion:

I. **Signal the end:** As we have seen, **[Reinforce Central Idea: Summary]** the ongoing crisis in Darfur is unimaginable: nearly 3 million people have been forced from their homes, countless rapes have occurred, and more than half a million lives have been lost in the conflict. But we have also seen that there is hope, that there are things each and every one of us can do, and that such efforts can have very real, very positive impacts on the people living there.

73

II.   A man far smarter than me once said, "Don't tell me what you value. Show me your budget and I'll show you what you value."

III.   **Call to Action:** And I would like to think that in the days and weeks ahead, every one of you can honestly show yourselves that you value protecting someone's mother, someone's sister, someone's daughter from the possibility of rape, or with supplying someone with a meal who might not otherwise have one, far more than you value another trip to McDonald's.

Bibliography

Hassan, Sallah M., ed., and Carina E. Ray, ed.. *Darfur and the Crisis of Governance in Sudan*. New York: Cornell UP., 2009. Print.

"Estimates for the Total Number of IDPs for all of Sudan (as of January 2010). Internal Displacement Monitoring Centre. 22 February 2010. Web. 20 July 2010.

"Q&A: Sudan's Darfur Conflict." BBC News. 23 February 2010. Web. 20 July 2010.

"Solar Cooker Project Evaluation." Jewish World Watch. October 2007. Web. 20 July 2010.

Steidle, Brian, and Gretchen Steidle Wallace. *The Devil Came on Horseback*. New York: Public Affairs, 2007. Print.

"UNICEF Adviser Says Rape in Darfur, Sudan Continues with Impunity." UN News Centre. 19 October 2004. Web. 20 July 2010.

"U.N.: 100,000 More Dead in Darfur Than Reported." CNN. 22 April 2008. Web. 20 July 2010.

"Countries: Sudan." World Food Programme. 2010. Web. 20 July 2010.

SAMPLE MONROE'S MOTIVATED
PERSUASIVE SPEECH OF POLICY OUTLINE

Name: Abbey Mattes
Date: November 9, 2005
Lab section # and Lab instructor's name: section 17, Katie Fuller

"Bone Marrow Registry"

Specific Purpose: To persuade my audience to become part of the bone marrow registry at the Des Moines or Simpson College donor drives.

Central Idea: Bone marrow transplants can help treat many people with life threatening diseases, and you can register locally to donate bone marrow and help save lives by through the National Bone Marrow Registry.

Pattern of Organization: Monroe's Motivated sequence

> This is an immediate action speech using Monroe's 5 step persuasive structure. Attention is handled in the Intro; Action is in the Conclusion. The body of the speech has three main points: Need, Satisfaction and Visualization.

Introduction/Attention (you need to use all parts of CARRP; this example shows how someone can be creative and interesting while accomplishing these steps):

I. **Attention and Relate to Audience**: Relate to the audience through imagining a scenario that puts them in the shoes of having someone in their family diagnosed disease that will kill them unless they get a bone marrow transplant, but no family member matches.

II. **Reveal Topic:** I am talking about the importance of becoming part of the national bone marrow registry; the organization which helps people who are in need of a life-saving marrow transplant.

III. **Expert Credibility and Significance**: My research has shown that 70 percent of the people who need bone marrow transplants can't get them from a family member and must turn to others to survive.

IV. **Relate to audience**: Most of us will know someone or will be in need ourselves.

V. **Credibility Personal**: As a member of the bone marrow registry, I am familiar with the donor process and experience. I have also researched numerous articles on the bone marrow registry.

VI. **Preview**: Today, I will explain to you the need for bone marrow registry, how becoming a part of the bone marrow registry may help, and I will describe exactly how you may become a part of the bone marrow registry.

(**Connective--Signpost**: First, we will look at the extreme need for individuals to sign up for the bone marrow registry.)

Need:

    I.   According to the *National Marrow Donor Program*, it is estimated that a marrow transplant could benefit more than 35,000 children and adults living with life-threatening diseases each year.

A. The Seattle Cancer Care Website states most types of cancer and conditions that affect the blood can be treated by a bone marrow transplant.

   1. Leukemia is the most common childhood cancer, and there are several types that may be treated with a bone marrow transplant.

   2. Other types of cancers such as lymphoma, brain tumors, and neuroblastoma may also be treated with a bone marrow transplant.

   3. Some non cancerous conditions that affect the blood such as sickle cell anemia, immunodeficiency syndromes, and hereditary blood disorders all may be treated with a bone marrow transplant.

B. 70 percent of patients in need cannot find a donor within their family and need to find an unrelated donor through the registry.

The speaker helps us understand the problem with numbers to enhance Logos and with stories to enhance pathos. By citing sources consistently, she also helps to build her ethos.

   1. Bone marrow tissue types are inherited but unfortunately most patients will not find a donor in their family.

   2. It is more likely that a donor will come from a patient's same ethnic background since tissue types are inherited.

      a. According to the *National Marrow Donor Program*, groups such as Alaska Native, Asian, Black, Hispanic, and Pacific Islander are all in need of more donors.
      b. Rod Carew, a prominent African American baseball player had a daughter who passed away while waiting for a bone marrow transplant, because of the lack of diversity in the donor pool.

C. According to a recent article "Our View: Bone Marrow Issue," about 1 in 9 patients in need of a bone marrow transplant are unable to find a perfect match.

   1. One explanation according to that same article in the *Iowa City Press* only about 2 percent of Americans are signed up for the bone marrow registry.

   2. 60 percent of Americans have the ability to donate.

(**Connective--Transition** Now you see the extreme need for bone marrow transplants, we can look at a way we can increase donor matches.)

Satisfaction:

II.   Organizations such as the *Iowa Marrow Donor Program* provide an easy and local way for individuals to join the registry.

A. Programs like this hold annual donor drives around the area for people to become registered.

    1. There are 2 donor drives during November and December.

        a. On November 17, 2005 Simpson College will host a drive from 11:00 a.m. to 4:00 p.m.

        b. On December 7, 2005 Des Moines University will be hosting a donor drive from noon to 5:00 p.m.

    2. You can also join the registry right here in Ames by contacting the Mary Greeley Health Center.

B. There are four quick and simple steps that allow you to become registered for the bone marrow registry at these drives.

    1. You will be given information about the marrow and peripheral (circulating) blood cell (known as PBSC) donation processes from the organization you choose to register through.

        a. This information usually comes in the form of a video.

        b. You may have a private consultation with a registered nurse if you wish.

> These kinds of details about the plan are especially important for immediate action speeches. Listeners can really figure out what they are being asked to do.

    2. You will complete a brief health questionnaire.

        a. This health questionnaire is similar to one you would fill out when you donate blood.

        b. I have a form that I will be handing out today so you may see exactly what questions are asked and you may determine if you are an eligible donor.

    3. You will sign a form consenting to have your tissue type listed on the Registry until your 61st birthday.

        a. If a donor is found, you will be contacted but you are not obligated to donate.

        b. You must remember that if you are matched you have the opportunity to donate to someone.

    4. You will provide a small blood sample, which is tested to determine your tissue type.

        a. This blood sample is similar to the sample you give when you donate blood.

b.   The sample is easily extracted and most of the blood will be returned to your body.

C.   Joining the National Bone Marrow Registry will increase the number of donors and therefore increase the possibility of a patient finding a match.

(**Connective--Transition**: Since we have looked at how we can increase the donor matches by increasing the number of individuals on the registry, we can now look at how individuals benefit from the bone marrow registry.)

Visualization:

III.   According to a newspaper article from *Iowa City Press*, lives have been saved by donating bone marrow.

A.   About three years ago, Jessica Franzen, a twenty year old college student that attended the University of Iowa was diagnosed with Leukemia.

1.   Jessica was forced to drop out of school and attend all day chemotherapy for several weeks.

2.   Doctors gave Jessica only a couple years left to live.

3.   She needed a bone marrow transplant and finally found a donor through the National Bone Marrow Registry.

4.   Jessica has now recovered and is living a happy life attending college for the second time.

B.   Another real life story of a successful bone marrow transplant match comes from the website hosted by the Iowa Donor Program.

1.   In 1995, a man named Scott from Urbandale Iowa decided to register as a marrow donor with the marrow donor program.

2.   Three years later, a nineteen-year-old woman, named Vinnie, from New York was diagnosed with leukemia and was in need of a marrow transplant and did not match any of her family members.

3.   Because Scott had joined the registry, Vinnie soon found a match with Scott.

4.   In 1998, Scott gave a portion of his bone marrow in hopes of saving Vinnie's life, and in 2000 Scott and Vinnie met for the first time.

The visualization step is the perfect place to share stories about what happens when people adopt the plan. Note how she selected stories from Iowa and stories that feature the age group of most audience members.

C. Since the national registry's inception in 1987, there are been 18,500 bone marrow transplants, according to the *National Bone Marrow Donor Registry.*

Conclusion/Action:

I. **Reinforce the Central Idea**: Thousands of people are waiting for a donor to make a difference in their lives; you can help

II. **Signal the end, summary**: As we have seen people who become part of the bone marrow registry, like Jessica and Vinnie, can really save lives.

III. **Final call to action**: Now I am asking all of you to take time to become a hero and possibly save someone's life. You have the ability to make an impact on another individual and their family. Becoming part of the National Bone Marrow Registry is an easy process, and you can sign up right here in Des Moines on December 7. The entire process is as easy as donating blood.

IV. **Strong Closing Line:** Imagine struggling with leukemia or any other disease and finding out that a match for bone marrow has been found. Each of you has the possibility of giving the gift of life and what a better time than the Christmas season.

Bibliography

Iowa Marrow Donor. 12 Oct. 2004. Iowa Donor. 6 Nov. 2005 <http://iowadonor.org>.

National Bone Marrow Donor Registry. 13 January 2006. Department of Health and Human Services. 31 May 2006 <http://www.whitehouse.gov/omb/expectmore/detail.html>.

National Marrow Donor Program. 15 May 2004. National Marrow Donor. 6 Nov. 2005 <http://www.marrow.org>.

"Our View: Bone Marrow Issue." 9 July 2005 *Iowa City Press.* 6 Nov. 2005 <http://iowacitypress.org>.

"Rod Carew's Daughter Michelle Dies of Leukemia." *Jet* .May 6, 1996: 62.

Seattle Care Center Alliance. 8 Oct. 2005. Children's Hospital and Regional Medical Center. 6 Nov. 2005 <http://seattlecca.org>.

Building the Argument for your Persuasive Speech of Policy:
Logos, Ethos and Pathos Appeals

The evidence you gather for your speech constitutes the fundamental resource for your persuasive case, but that evidence becomes a strong argument to firmly support your claims through your development of appeals to Logos, Ethos and Pathos. To create a strong speech that has the potential to be persuasive to a diverse audience, you will need to incorporate each of these three types of appeals into your speech.

As discussed in chapter 16, *logos* is the Greek word for reasoning or logical appeal. When we create arguments grounded in *logos* we are engaged in recognizable forms of reasoning. We might be creating inductive or generalization arguments, causal arguments, arguments from principle or arguments from analogy. When you offer evidence that teenagers make up only 7% of licensed drivers in the US, but account for 14% of driving fatalities, you are building an appeal from *logos* to support your claim that more needs to be done to protect teen drivers. Statistics is the form of evidence most closely related to appeals to logos since people trust the apparent non-biased evidence of numerical data and consider it to be highly rational.

Ethos arguments are those appeals that rely on the credibility of the speaker as the central feature that leads the audience to accept the argument. If your audience finds you to be trustworthy (character) and to have expertise (competence), they are more likely to believe your claim. If you are a volunteer for the local women's shelter, sharing that background with the class will demonstrate your commitment to the issue and help establish a positive evaluation of your character. And when you use strong credible evidence from experts to support your claims about the causes of domestic abuse and the steps we need to take to reduce the problem, you establish your competence; doing good research and supporting your claims helps contribute to your *ethos*. Finally, when you deliver the speech with passion and confidence you help support the audience's perception of your *ethos* and add further support to your claims. Testimony is the type of evidence most associated with your *ethos* appeal.

Pathos appeals supply the third leg for support for your claims. These appeals touch our emotions and, according to Aristotle, put us in the right frame of mind to be persuaded. *Pathos* appeals, such as an example of someone being injured or hurt—perhaps a story of a child suffering from malnutrition—help motivate listeners to hear our arguments and feel compelled to act. In addition to the use of examples as evidence, use of images, powerful language choices and passionate delivery can help you generate your *pathos* appeal and increase your persuasiveness. In the Plan section of a speech such appeals can help listeners believe that they can make a difference.

In the sample speeches you can see how these three kinds of appeals work together to support an argument. One way to make sure you are incorporating all three appeals into your speech is by including statistics to help support your *logos* appeal, testimony to support your *ethos* appeal and examples to support your *pathos* appeal. Which of these types of appeals will have the most impact depends on your claim, your credibility and the levels of motivation, knowledge of the subject and even the personal preferences of the members of your audience. This variability in impact is one reason why it is important to build support for each of your claims using each of these appeals.

Persuasive Speech Analysis Questions

As you read sample speeches in the textbook, view sample speeches in lecture, or listen to speeches in lab, practice paying attention to the choices speakers make as they aim to persuade. Be sure to ask yourself questions such as these.

1. What are the main points of the speech? What is the pattern of organization used here and how does it help the speech accomplish its persuasive goal?

2. What is the Problem (need) Issue of this speech?

3. What are the parts of the speaker's Plan?

4. How does the speaker show that this Plan is Practical? How could this step be made stronger?

5. Evaluate the speaker's use of examples, testimony, and statistics to develop the claims about the Problem, Plan and Practicality. How well are the appeals from pathos, ethos and logos developed here? What could be added to strengthen the speech?

6. What special steps did the speaker take to use materials and language aimed to engage the audience?

7. What special steps did the speaker take to use delivery to build credibility, engage you as a listener and help you understand the topic?

8. How well are all of the functions of an Introduction and Conclusion accomplished in this speech? Point out the best and the weakest features of the Intro and Conclusion.

9. Does the speech persuade you? Why or why not?

Classic Sample Persuasive Speech of Policy
Can you see the Problem, Plan and Practicality Arguments Made Here?

Give Me Liberty or Give Me Death
Patrick Henry, March 23, 1775 at the Virginia Convention

Based on the text prepared by William Wirt, Henry's Biographer

No man thinks more highly than I do of the patriotism, as well as abilities, of the very worthy gentlemen who have just addressed the House. But different men often see the same subject in different lights; and, therefore, I hope it will not be thought disrespectful to those gentlemen if, entertaining as I do opinions of a character very opposite to theirs, I shall speak forth my sentiments freely and without reserve. This is no time for ceremony. The question before the House is one of awful moment to this country. For my own part, I consider it as nothing less than a question of freedom or slavery; and in proportion to the magnitude of the subject ought to be the freedom of the debate. It is only in this way that we can hope to arrive at truth, and fulfill the great responsibility which we hold to God and our country. Should I keep back my opinions at such a time, through fear of giving offense, I should consider myself as guilty of treason towards my country, and of an act of disloyalty toward the Majesty of Heaven, which I revere above all earthly kings.

Mr. President, it is natural to man to indulge in the illusions of hope. We are apt to shut our eyes against a painful truth, and listen to the song of that siren till she transforms us into beasts. Is this the part of wise men, engaged in a great and arduous struggle for liberty? Are we disposed to be of the number of those who, having eyes, see not, and, having ears, hear not, the things which so nearly concern their temporal salvation? For my part, whatever anguish of spirit it may cost, I am willing to know the whole truth; to know the worst, and to provide for it.

I have but one lamp by which my feet are guided, and that is the lamp of experience. I know of no way of judging of the future but by the past. And judging by the past, I wish to know what there has been in the conduct of the British ministry for the last ten years to justify those hopes with which gentlemen have been pleased to solace themselves and the House. Is it that insidious smile with which our petition has been lately received? Trust it not, sir; it will prove a snare to your feet. Suffer not yourselves to be betrayed with a kiss. Ask yourselves how this gracious reception of our petition comports with those warlike preparations which cover our waters and darken our land. Are fleets and armies necessary to a work of love and reconciliation? Have we shown ourselves so unwilling to be reconciled that force must be called in to win back our love? Let us not deceive ourselves, sir. These are the implements of war and subjugation; the last arguments to which Kings resort. I ask gentlemen, sir, what means this martial array, if its purpose be not to force us to submission? Can gentlemen assign any other possible motive for it? Has Great Britain any enemy, in this quarter of the world, to call for all this accumulation of navies and armies? No, sir, she has none. They are meant for us: they can be meant for no other. They are sent over to bind and rivet upon us those chains which the British ministry have been so long forging. And what have we to oppose to them? Shall we try argument? Sir, we have been trying that for the last ten years. Have we anything new to offer upon the subject? Nothing. We have held the subject up in every light of which it is capable; but it has been all in vain. Shall we resort to entreaty and humble supplication? What terms shall we find which have not been already exhausted? Let us not, I beseech you, sir, deceive ourselves. Sir, we have done everything that could be done to avert the storm which is now coming on. We have petitioned; we have remonstrated; we have supplicated; we have prostrated ourselves before the throne, and have implored its interposition to arrest the tyrannical hands of the ministry and Parliament. Our petitions have been slighted; our remonstrances have produced additional violence and insult; our supplications have been disregarded; and we have been spurned, with contempt, from the foot of the throne! In vain, after these things, may we indulge the fond hope of peace and reconciliation. There is no longer any room for hope. If we wish to be free-- if we mean to preserve inviolate those inestimable privileges for which we have been so long contending--if we mean not basely to abandon the noble struggle in which we have been so long engaged, and which we have pledged ourselves never to abandon until the glorious object of our contest shall be obtained--we must fight! I repeat it, sir, we must fight! An appeal to arms and to the God of hosts is all that is left us!

They tell us, sir, that we are weak; unable to cope with so formidable an adversary. But when shall we be stronger? Will it be the next week, or the next year? Will it be when we are totally disarmed, and when a British guard shall be stationed in every house? Shall we gather strength by irresolution and inaction? Shall we acquire the means of effectual resistance by lying supinely on our backs and hugging the delusive phantom of hope, until our enemies shall have bound us hand and foot? Sir, we are not weak if we make a proper use of those means which the God of nature hath placed in our power. The millions of people, armed in the holy cause of liberty, and in such a country as that which we possess, are invincible by any force which our enemy can send against us. Besides, sir, we shall not fight our battles alone. There is a just God who presides over the destinies of nations, and who will raise up friends to fight our battles for us. The battle, sir, is not to the strong alone; it is to the vigilant, the active, the brave. Besides, sir, we have no election.* If we were base enough to desire it, it is now too late to retire from the contest. There is no retreat but in submission and slavery! Our chains are forged! Their clanking may be heard on the plains of Boston! The war is inevitable--and let it come! I repeat it, sir, let it come.

It is in vain, sir, to extenuate the matter. Gentlemen may cry, Peace, Peace-- but there is no peace. The war is actually begun! The next gale that sweeps from the north will bring to our ears the clash of resounding arms! Our brethren are already in the field! Why stand we here idle? What is it that gentlemen wish? What would they have? Is life so dear, or peace so sweet, as to be purchased at the price of chains and slavery? Forbid it, Almighty God! I know not what course others may take; but as for me, give me liberty or give me death!

* "election" means "choice" in this context.

Workshop: Persuasive Policy Speech Worksheet

Use the following questions to review the outlines for the persuasive speech of policy.

1. What is the specific purpose statement for the speech? What is the central idea? Do they meet the definition of the assignment?

2. What is the Problem (need) issue in the speech? How is the speaker supporting the claims? What evidence is being used to support the claims? Is it a good variety of evidence? Will the audience accept the sources as credible?

3. What is the Plan? Are specific actions being called for? What are the steps in it? Who is being called to act?

4. How will the speaker prove that the Plan will solve the Problem?   What evidence is used to prove this? Is it a good variety of evidence? Are the sources credible? Will the practicality discussion make sense to the class?

5. Does the speaker plan to address the opposition to the plan? How will the speaker prove that the advantages of the plan outweigh the disadvantages that come to mind?

6. Does the introduction work to capture audience attention and interest? to establish speaker credibility? to preview the speech? How might the speaker improve the introduction?

7. Does the conclusion wrap things together nicely? Does it signal the end of the speech? Is it striking/memorable? What might the speaker try to make it better?

8. How are the parts of the speech going to be connected to one another? Are good transitions and internal previews being planned?

9. What kinds of visual aids does the speaker plan to use to clarify the ideas of the speech?

10. What kind of strategies does the speaker plan to employ to maintain audience attention and interest throughout the speech?

11. Does the outline include at least four high quality sources that are cited in the Body? Is the bibliography clear and well developed?

Final Outline Checklist for the Persuasive Speech

Use this checklist to guide you in reviewing your final outline. These are the same criteria your instructor will use to grade your outline.

Specific Purpose (SP) and Central Idea (CI) Statements [3 pt.] • Are they stated at the top of the outline? • Does the Specific Purpose follow the guidelines? (Proper format and calls for the goal, a policy focus). • Does the Central Idea follow the guidelines? (One sentence that reveals content & structure of the speech.)	
Pattern of Organization [2 pt.] • Is the pattern of organization correctly identified and using a pattern from Chapter 15? • Do the Roman Numerals in the outline follow that pattern?	
Introduction [2 pt.] • CARRP: are all 5 parts included and labeled accurately? • Does planned credibility develop both personal and expert dimensions?	
Main Points [2 pts.] • Are points stated in single complete sentences and using symbols properly? • Are the main points in body developed in the same order as was promised by the Preview Statement?	
Sub-points [5 pts.] • Are sub-points stated in single complete sentences? • Do they use symbols properly and follow the rule of division? (if there is an A there is a B, if there is a 1 there is a 2) • Do the sub-points clearly fit under the main point as it is stated? • Is there material included that addresses each of the major issues: Problem, Plan and Practicality? • Is the speaker making sense of the argument and evidence for us? (language clear; points are not simply cut and pasted from sources)	
Connectives [2 pt.] • Are the connectives included before and between each of the main points? • Are connectives identified and properly labeled?	
Conclusion [2pt.] • Does it Signal the End, Reinforce the Central Idea and Call for Action? • Are the parts properly labeled?	
Sources / Bibliography [2 pt.] • Are sources noted in the body of the outline as well as the bibliography? • Does the citation in the bibliography provide enough information to locate the source?	

Unit III:
Speaking on Special Occasions

The Special Occasion Speech Assignment Requirements

This third speech assignment offers you a choice. You may select to create and present a Speech to Inspire (commemorative speech) or a Speech to Entertain (an After-Dinner speech). The assignments and their specific requirements are described in the following pages. Your Lab Instructor may have special instructions about this assignment for your section. All of the speeches in this final speech round have the following requirements:

1.   The Topic Form must be completed and submitted through the SpCm 212 Blackboard site by the date indicated on the syllabus. Be sure to check back for feedback on your topic.

2.   The time limit for the speech is 4.5 minutes. You should time your speech as you practice it to be sure that it falls within a minute of the time limit. Since this is a manuscript speech you have only 30 seconds on either side of the 4.5 minute limit. This still gives you time to add an aside or restate a point as needed while you speak. Failure to meet the time limit will result in a 1/3 letter grade penalty that will increase at 30 second intervals [so the first penalties begin at 3:59 and 5:01, the next 1/3 deduction is added at 3:29 and at 5:31, etc.]

3.   Use of creative language is required. Chapter 11 presents some of the stylistic devices you might employ. The sample speeches provide good examples of this creative use of language. As a minimum you are expected to include 5 stylistic devices of at least three different types.

4.   Two drafts of your manuscript are due for the workshop day as indicated on the syllabus.

5.   Two copies of the final manuscript of the speech are due at the beginning of your lab section on the day you are assigned to speak. The manuscript should have a clear Specific Purpose Statement, Central Idea and Pattern of Organization at the top of the page and the stylistic devices used should be in **bold and labeled** (identified as simile, metaphor, parallelism, etc.).

6.   You may deliver the speech from a speaking outline or from a delivery manuscript.* In either case, you are not to read the speech to the audience; the goal remains that of a conversational style of delivery. Remember that delivering with the purpose of inspiring or entertaining the audience may require special use of inflection, facial expression, and gesture.

7.   Originality is essential to the assignment. The speech must be developed with your ideas and your wording. There are no research requirements for this speech assignment, but if you use any sources you must cite them in the bibliography and you must orally inform the audience when you are quoting or paraphrasing from a source.

In addition to the above requirements, the grading criteria for the speech are: clarity of ideas, creativity and appropriateness of thought, language and supporting materials, sense of structure or flow of ideas, appropriate impact on audience, fulfillment of the requirements for the type of speech you choose (see the following pages for a discussion of the specific assignments), and use of delivery to enhance impact.

*A delivery manuscript is one that has larger type and margins than a regular paper. Use highlighting to signal the main points in the text and use the large margins to write delivery reminders to yourself.

Special Occasion Speech Option 1
The Speech To Inspire

Speeches to Inspire, or commemorative speeches, are speeches that build community by inviting the audience to share in a celebration of the values exemplified in a person, institution, or event. They are typically inspiring to the audience gathered for the special occasion.

Your assignment is to pay tribute to a significant person, group of people, institution, or idea in a 4.5 minute speech. You are speaking to the students in your lab section, though, so you are not to pretend that you are at a retirement party, wedding or funeral. Your topic may be someone or something admirable and famous--like Martin Luther King, Jr., Mother Theresa, or the Bill of Rights--or it may be someone or something the audience may not have heard of--your uncle, your seventh grade teacher, the person who discovered a vaccine or an institution such as the Carnegie Foundation. The focus of the assignment is creative language use, so rather than producing an outline and delivering the speech extemporaneously, you will prepare a manuscript. Your speech should use language imaginatively, clearly, and vividly. It is through your use of language that you can stir the sentiments of your audience.

The key to the speech is to focus on two or three major traits of your subject. Loyalty, intelligence, beauty, kindness, uniqueness, dedication, tradition, innovation, humor, philanthropy, innocence, experience, altruism, or bravery are the kinds of traits around which you might build your speech. Once you have settled on two or three characteristics, you can develop the speech by using support materials such as stories and examples to show how the subject of your speech embodies those values. The speech is not simply informative; its function is to celebrate with your audience the particular praiseworthy traits/values of your subject. Part of your purpose is to inspire your audience. This means you might reaffirm their values, encourage them to value something or someone overlooked, or offer such praise to particular characteristics that your audience is moved to imitate them.

The materials of the speech are values/characteristics, examples, and language. The speech is not to be a biography or a recital of historical events. The speech ought not be controversial. (We do not commemorate Hitler, for instance, nor do we praise someone for being a "really successful drug dealer.")

In addition to meeting all of the requirements for the Special Occasion Assignment discussed on the previous page, the strong commemorative speech aims to:

•   give compelling expression to ideas through organization. Carefully structure the speech for the greatest impact.

•   give compelling expression to ideas through delivery. Manuscript delivery is challenging. Do not read the speech to the audience.

•   give compelling expression to ideas through your language. Use the strategies discussed in Chapter 11 to go beyond the way you "normally" talk.

•   See the following page for the feedback form your instructor will use.

Special Occasion Speech to Inspire Feedback Form

This is a copy of the feedback form your lab instructor will use to respond to your special occasion speech if your overall goal is to inspire the audience. On your speaking day be sure to bring a copy of this form from the back of your workbook and give it to your lab instructor.

Speaker _____

Topic _____

Rate the speaker on each point:	*O-outstanding*		*S-satisfactory*	*N–needs work*
Introduction gained attention	O	S	N	
Subject introduced clearly	O	S	N	
Main ideas easily followed	O	S	N	
Conclusion reinforced the central idea	O	S	N	
Topic dealt with creatively	O	S	N	
Stylistic devices included	O	S	N	
Stylistic devices used effectively	O	S	N	
Support materials helpful	O	S	N	
Originality of thought and expression	O	S	N	
Sufficient eye contact	O	S	N	
Voice used effectively	O	S	N	
Nonverbal communication effective	O	S	N	
Presentation of self strong	O	S	N	
Speech adapted to audience	O	S	N	
Speech had intended impact on audience	O	S	N	

Comments

Special Occasion Speech Option 2
The Speech to Entertain

Your assignment is to prepare and deliver a 4.5 minute speech that entertains an audience or inspires your audience in a light-hearted way. The After-Dinner speech is something like a humorous informative speech. It is not a stand-up comedy routine—since it still has a specific purpose in mind, an introduction, body and conclusion, and distinguishable main points. The specific purposes for a speech to entertain would include options such as: "To entertain my audience by showing the ridiculous extremes some people go to in following special diets" or "To entertain my audience by detailing the painful lessons I learned as I discovered that I was never going to be an athlete" or "To entertain my audience by exploring how my love-hate relationship with horror movies has had a major impact on my life" or "To entertain my audience by sharing tales of my family's odd reunion traditions" or "To entertain my audience with stories underscoring my serious culture shock during my ill-advised study abroad program my freshman year." Or you might entertain the audience with a speech that classifies and characterizes drivers you have encountered or customers you have waited on or odd holiday customs in your family.

The materials for the speech to entertain are your personal observations and experiences developed in a humorous way and with an eye toward the special use of language. Use stylistic devices like those discussed in chapter 11 of the textbook to create clear images in the minds of your listeners. Other stylistic devices such as hyperbole can also be useful to the after-dinner speaker. Humorists such as Mark Twain and Dave Barry are part of the tradition of After-dinner speaking in the U.S. If you read their works you can see how they use humor to make insightful points.

In preparing your speech be sure to do the following:

1.   Have a clear and definite specific purpose and central idea.

2.   Create an <u>original</u> speech—full of your ideas and phrasing.

3.   The introduction should get our attention and interest, make sure we understand the topic, and preview the main ideas of the speech. (Of course, it should establish the humorous tone of the speech.)

4.   Follow a clear pattern of organization (probably topical with 2-4 main points).

5.   *The body of the speech should demonstrate creative thinking and creative language use.*

6.   Your conclusion should sum up the speech and give the audience something to think about after the speech is over.

7.   Rehearse the speech to create a smooth flow of words, and to develop an engaging delivery style so that you create the entertaining impact that is the goal of the assignment.

8.   Make sure your humor is appropriate. Do not offend your audience and beware of dark humor; what seems hilarious at 2 a.m. can seem highly inappropriate under the fluorescent lights in the classroom.

9.   See the following page for the feedback form your instructor will use when grading.

Special Occasion Speech to Entertain Feedback Form

This is a copy of the feedback form your lab instructor will use to respond to your special occasion speech if your overall goal is to entertain the audience. On your speaking day be sure to bring a copy of this form from the back of your workbook and give it to your lab instructor.

Speaker _____

Topic _____

Rate the speaker on each point: O-outstanding S-satisfactory   N–needs work

Introduction gained attention	O	S	N
Subject introduced clearly	O	S	N
Main ideas easily followed	O	S	N
Conclusion reinforced the central idea	O	S	N
Topic dealt with creatively	O	S	N
Stylistic devices included	O	S	N
Stylistic devices used effectively	O	S	N
Supporting materials entertaining	O	S	N
Humor appropriate	O	S	N
Originality of thought and expression	O	S	N
Sufficient eye contact	O	S	N
Voice used effectively	O	S	N
Nonverbal communication effective	O	S	N
Presentation of self strong	O	S	N
Speech adapted to audience	O	S	N
Speech had intended impact on audience	O	S	N

Comments

Challenger Address: January 28, 1986
by President Ronald Reagan

[The main speech writer for this text was Peggy Noonan; for more information on the creation of this text see Noonan's fascinating account in chapter 13 of What I Saw at the Revolution: A Political Life in the Reagan Era]

Specific Purpose: To inspire my audience to honor the astronauts who lost their lives in the explosion:

Central Idea: We honor the Challenger Seven by valuing their contributions and by continuing to follow their noble goals.

1. Ladies and Gentlemen, I'd planned to speak to you tonight to report on the State of the Union. But the events of earlier today have led me to change those plans. Today is a day for mourning and remembering. Nancy and I are pained to the core by the tragedy of the shuttle Challenger. We know we share this pain with all the people of our country. This is truly a national loss. Nineteen years ago almost to the day, we lost three astronauts in a terrible accident on the ground. But we've never lost an astronaut in flight. We've never had a tragedy like this. And perhaps we've forgotten the courage it took for the crew of the shuttle. But they, the Challenger seven, were aware of the dangers and overcame them and did their jobs brilliantly.

2. We mourn seven heroes: Michael Smith, Dick Scobee, Judith Resnik, Ronald McNair, Ellison Onizuka, Gregory Jarvis and Christa McAuliffe. We mourn their loss as a nation together. To the families of the seven, we cannot bear as you do the full impact of this tragedy. But we feel the loss and we're thinking about you so very much. Your loved ones were daring and brave, and they had that special grace, that special spirit that says give me a challenge and I'll meet it with joy. They had a hunger to explore the universe and discover its truths. They wished to serve and they did. They served all of us.

3. We've grown used to wonders in this century. It's hard to dazzle us. But for 25 years the United States space program has been doing just that. We've grown used to the idea of space and perhaps we forget that we've only just begun. We're still pioneers. They, the members of the Challenger crew, were pioneers. And I want to say something to the school children of America who were watching the live coverage of the shuttle's takeoff. I know it's hard to understand, but sometimes painful things like this happen. It's all part of taking a chance and expanding man's horizons. The future doesn't belong to the fainthearted. It belongs to the brave. The Challenger crew was pulling us into the future and we'll continue to follow them.

4. I've always had great faith in and respect for our space program. And, what happened today does nothing to diminish it. We don't hide our space program. We don't keep

secrets and cover things up. We do it all up front and in public. That's the way freedom is and we wouldn't change it for a minute. We'll continue our quest in space. There will be more shuttle flights and more shuttle crews, and, yes, more volunteers, more civilians, more teachers in space. Nothing ends here. Our hopes and our journeys continue. I want to add that I wish I could talk to every man and woman who works for NASA or who worked on this mission, and tell them: "Your dedication and professionalism have moved and impressed us for decades and we know of your anguish. We share it."

5. There's a coincidence today. On this date 390 years ago, the great explorer Sir Francis Drake died aboard ship off the coast of Panama. In his lifetime, the great frontiers were the oceans and a historian later said "He lived by the sea, died on it and was buried in it." Well, today we can say of the Challenger crew, their dedication was, like Drake's, complete.

6. The crew of the space shuttle Challenger honored us with the manner in which they lived their lives. We will never forget them or the last time we saw them, this morning, as they prepared for their journey and waved goodbye and "slipped the surly bonds of Earth to touch the face of God."

Sample Student Speech To Inspire

Stories of My Mother
by Marc Malone, Summer 2010, section 14

Specific Purpose: To inspire my audience to recognize the power of stories to build memories about the people who matter most.

Central Idea: Though my mother died before I finished high school, the stories people share about her frugality and strength have helped me remember more about who she was and why listening to each other matters.

Pattern of organization: Topical

I believe in the power of stories. I believe in the power of shared experiences. I believe in the power of knowing life through someone else's point of view [repetition]. My fascination with stories started when my mother died. I was only seventeen, far too young to really appreciate her as anyone other than the woman who yelled at me **when my music was too loud, my room was too messy, my driving speed too high [parallelism].** It's surprising how fast someone can slip out of your mind. The feel of her hands, the sound of her voice, the way she looked at the mirror when she did her makeup—those things I remember. Those moments matter, but I want to know more. Who was she? How did she become who she was? How much did family matter to her? The answers to such questions can **fade** too **fast** as **friends** and **family** try to protect themselves **from feeling** pain **[alliteration].** To find answers, I turned to stories. I'm going to tell you about my passion for stories by telling you two about my mother that illustrate their power.

My mother was frugal. When I talk with my brother and sister, we often reminisce about family shopping trips. Mom took us shopping precisely once a year—always right before the school year began. Dad took us shopping all the time, for anything. **Mom met our needs; Dad indulged our wants [antithesis].** Because of this difference, my mom earned the reputation as the uncool, strict, no-fun parent. This doesn't mean we didn't love her, we just never asked her for money. One day, while talking to my grandmother, she told me a story about my mother that helped me understand why my mom was such a stickler for monetary restraint. My mother had a hard life. She grew up in a small house on a 160-acre farm lovingly nicknamed Poverty Point. It really was the heart of poverty. I had always known that my grandparents struggled financially, but I didn't know the full extent of it until after my mother died. Growing up on that farm, my grandmother explained, was growing up in the proverbial school of hard knocks. My mother's family qualified for government assistance, but my grandfather was too stubborn to accept it. Whatever they needed, then, they came up with on their own. **Going to sleep meant sharing a bed with a sibling. Preparing breakfast meant baking bread and gathering eggs from the chicken coop. Getting dressed meant putting on clothes that were homemade or, if**

you were lucky, were hand-me-downs from cousins. Going to school meant catching the bus [parallelism]. There were no car rides to school; if you missed the bus, you rode your bike, quickly. I think we all have our own troubles, but when I sat with my grandma that day wishing for a new car and hoping for another trip to Europe, my troubles seemed especially trivial. Her story reminded me of what my mother often said to her children: be thankful for what you have and be patient for more.

My mother was strong and caring. When diagnosed with ovarian cancer she was the first to make light of her situation. The cancer had grown in two large tumors—one the size of a football, one the size of a softball. Before her first surgery she would make jokes that the doctor was going to remove her football and softball and that, once they were gone, she would need some new sports equipment. This joke, told over and over to friends and family who expressed concern, was a way of coping with what must have been an intense fear. She was so good at joking, in fact, that I didn't know just how afraid she really was. After she died, my father told me a story. One day, after some bad news from the doctor, my father found my mother in the kitchen unloading the dishwasher, a few quiet tears slipping down her face. When she looked up at him she told him, "I just want to make it to Marc's graduation." She didn't. When I walked across that stage and looked out at the all too obvious, all too vacant seat where my mother should have been, it would have been easy **to get lost in a sea of melancholy and self-pity [metaphor].** It was that story that pulled me out of my funk; it told me that my mother was so proud of me that my achievement was worth living for. That story was enough to send me across that stage with a smile on my face.

As a literature major, stories have become a huge part of my life. **I read them, I write them, I write about them [parallelism].** Most importantly, though, I have realized that stories are all around us, connecting us to one another, helping us answer the big questions we ask. In a time when instantaneous mass communication lives at our fingertips, it is easy to leave the past behind, to move too quickly into the future. Through my time with stories, be they about my mother, about my sister's allergy-prone dog Molly, or about my dad's latest camping adventure, I have learned the power of sharing experiences, of slowing down the world long enough to really listen and connect to another person. **We all have** stories to tell, **we all have** a point of view worth sharing, **we all have** a chance to learn from the stories we hear **[repetition]. My fascination with stories started as the mechanism to remember my mother, now they serve as the mechanism to create new memories [antithesis].**

Sample Student Speech To Inspire

Discovering Our Place in the Universe
by Rob Lourens, Spring 2010, Section 24, TA: Julia Wiegers

Specific Purpose: To inspire my audience by showing how the US space program has helped me discover my place in the universe.

Central Idea: We all need help discovering our place in the universe and for me that help came from the space program.

Pattern of organization: Chronological

Imagine yourself walking down a dimly lit corridor. On either side of you are bookshelves which stretch higher than you can reach. You stop and grab a dusty book at random but you are too young to understand even the title. Further down the shelf, you try again, but are rewarded with nothing but another dusty book and another indecipherable title. You continue on like this with no luck.

You found yourself dropped unsuspectingly onto this **cold, complicated, and confusing [alliteration]** planet some 6 or 7 years ago and you've been struggling to make sense of it ever since. Somewhere, among these numerous rows filled with grown-up knowledge, there must be some explanation for it all, some bit of wisdom that will light your path, some answer to the question: what is my place in the universe? **You've been searching for order, but you've discovered only randomness, or reasons too complex for you to grasp [antithesis], [repetition of forms of the word "discovery" occurs throughout the speech].**

A book catches your eye—it has a picture of the Earth on the spine, and you figure that this is as good a place as any to start. You discover that this book is part of a series on the planets, so you grab as many as you can carry and wander off to find your mom.

This is actually me. It's the mid-90's, and the place is the Urbandale Public Library. I practically grew up in that library, especially in that section of non-fiction books about space. I would soon spend hours poring over every detail of those books—examining the pictures closely, reading their descriptions and imaging what it might be like to jog on the Moon, ice skate on Pluto or ride a comet. **I was a space explorer in my own mind, wandering the universe as I wandered the library, discovering its secrets [metaphor].**

Can you point to such a moment in your past that has led you to where you are now? Some of my friends tell me I am lucky since from that time forward the space program has put me on a path of **discovery**. It inspired me and sparked my imagination as a kid, taught me things I never would have learned otherwise in high school, and has helped to determine my career path in college.

For a long time, of course, I wanted to be an astronaut when I grew up. I **discovered** that goal was unrealistic—my weak eyes and tendency toward motion sickness would not allow it—but I still could see my older self doing only one thing: working for NASA or within the space program in some capacity.

As I got older, I **discovered** my obsession with space and science fiction, trying to read the latest on the Spirit and Opportunity landers, the Cassini-Huygens mission, or the space shuttle between high school classes. On shuttle launch days, I would sometimes even join the group of "cool kids" and skip class. **But while the rest of the group would sneak out to the park to drink and smoke, I would sneak into the empty computer lab and watch the launch online [antithesis].** I watched the Space Shuttle Columbia take off on its last mission, and I happened to be awake early that Saturday morning when it was to land. I turned on the TV to see the shuttle's remains like **shining scars on the face of the sky [simile].** It was an incredibly depressing thing for a kid who was determined to work for NASA to see, and honestly, it almost turned me off of the space program forever. But I followed the aftermath closely over the next few years and admired the systematic and orderly way that their engineers went about determining and fixing the cause of the problem. They examined the evidence, **put the puzzle together one piece at a time [metaphor],** and took steps to prevent it from happening again in the future. **While most people looked at the disaster and saw a giant explosion, seven pointless deaths, and failure, engineers saw giant piles of data, serious problems to solve, and a preventable failure of engineering [parallelism].** I was fascinated by this point of view that seemed so reasonable, clean, and drama-free compared to the traumatic and seemingly random event itself. The space program helped me **discover** what engineering is about, and I only became more determined than ever to become involved with it.

I started off at ISU as an aerospace engineer, with my goal of NASA in mind, but soon came to a new **discovery**: I wasn't really interested in the physical mechanical systems of a spacecraft; I was drawn to computers! I needed to change my major, but didn't want to abandon my dream. Some research soon assured me that NASA needed software engineers as much as they need aerospace engineers. One article that influenced me in particular was a story about the people who write the software for the shuttle. It has been extended, maintained, and polished, and today is considered by many software engineers to be the only piece of complex industrial software in the world that is entirely bug-free.

With my new major my path of **discovery** is continuing. This summer, I'll be an intern at a large aerospace company, working with cockpit displays on commercial aircraft. It isn't NASA yet, but it's a step in the right direction.

As I think about it today, I do feel lucky and I hope that each of you **dares to discover your own destiny during [alliteration]** your time here at ISU. The space program has always been there to remind me that the universe is a fascinating and enormous place. As a kid, it expanded my mind, and got me to think **outside the box—outside Urbandale, outside Iowa, outside our tiny planet [parallelism].** In high school, it taught me what engineering is about—something I could never have learned in class. In college, it guided my choices and gave me a direction and a goal. And hopefully some day it will be my job to make sure that there is plenty of new and interesting material for other kids to **discover** in the dimly lit corridors at the back of the library.

President's Remarks at National Day of Prayer and Remembrance
The National Cathedral, Washington, D.C. September 14, 2001
by George W. Bush

From: http://www.whitehouse.gov/news/releases/2001/09/20010914-2.html

(you can also listen to the speech at this web site)

Specific Purpose: To inspire the audience to honor those who lost their lives in the terrorist attacks and rescue efforts.

Central Idea: We are a people in deep sorrow who honor those who died while we work toward a firm resolve based in a renewed faith in God and a renewed sense of our unity as a nation.

1. We are here in the middle hour of our grief. So many have suffered so great a loss, and today we express our Nation's sorrow. We come before God to pray for the missing and the dead, and for those who love them.

2. On Tuesday, our country was attacked with deliberate and massive cruelty. We have seen the images of fire and ashes, and bent steel.

3. Now come the names, the list of casualties we are only beginning to read. They are the names of men and women who began their day at a desk or in an airport, busy with life. They are the names of people who faced death, and in their last moments called home to say, be brave, and I love you. They are the names of passengers who defied their murderers, and prevented the murder of others on the ground. They are the names of men and women who wore the uniform of the United States, and died at their posts. They are the names of rescuers, the ones whom death found running up the stairs and into the fires to help others. We will read all these names. We will linger over them, and learn their stories, and many Americans will weep.

4. To the children and parents and spouses and families and friends of the lost, we offer the deepest sympathy of the nation. And I assure you, you are not alone.

5. Just three days removed from these events, Americans do not yet have the distance of history. But our responsibility to history is already clear: to answer these attacks and rid the world of evil. War has been waged against us by stealth and deceit and murder. This nation is peaceful, but fierce when stirred to anger. This conflict was begun on the timing and terms of others. It will end in a way, and at an hour, of our choosing.

6. Our purpose as a nation is firm. Yet our wounds as a people are recent and unhealed, and lead us to pray. In many of our prayers this week, there is a searching, and an honesty. At St. Patrick's Cathedral in New York on Tuesday, a woman said, "I prayed to God to give us a sign that He is still here." Others have prayed for the same, searching hospital to hospital, carrying pictures of those still missing.

7. God's signs are not always the ones we look for. We learn in tragedy that his purposes are not always our own. Yet the prayers of private suffering, whether in our homes or in this great cathedral, are known and heard, and understood. There are prayers that help us last through the day, or endure the night. There are prayers of friends and strangers, that give us strength for the journey. And there are prayers that yield our will to a will greater than our own. This world He created is of moral design. Grief and tragedy and hatred are only for a time. Goodness, remembrance, and love have no end. And the Lord of life holds all who die, and all who mourn.

8. It is said that adversity introduces us to ourselves. This is true of a nation as well. In this trial, we have been reminded, and the world has seen, that our fellow Americans are generous and kind, resourceful and brave. We see our national character in rescuers working past exhaustion; in long lines of blood donors; in thousands of citizens who have asked to work and serve in any way possible.

9. And we have seen our national character in eloquent acts of sacrifice. Inside the World Trade Center, one man who could have saved himself stayed until the end at the side of his quadriplegic friend. A beloved priest died giving the last rites to a firefighter. Two office workers, finding a disabled stranger, carried her down sixty-eight floors to safety. A group of men drove through the night from Dallas to Washington to bring skin grafts for burn victims.

10. In these acts, and in many others, Americans showed a deep commitment to one another, and an abiding love for our country. Today, we feel what Franklin Roosevelt called the warm courage of national unity. This is a unity of every faith, and every background. It has joined together political parties in both houses of Congress. It is evident in services of prayer and candlelight vigils, and American flags, which are displayed in pride, and wave in defiance. Our unity is a kinship of grief, and a steadfast resolve to prevail against our enemies. And this unity against terror is now extending across the world.

11. America is a nation full of good fortune, with so much to be grateful for. But we are not spared from suffering. In every generation, the world has produced enemies of human freedom. They have attacked America, because we are freedom's home and defender. And the commitment of our fathers is now the calling of our time.

12. On this national day of prayer and remembrance, we ask almighty God to watch over our nation, and grant us patience and resolve in all that is to come. We pray that He will comfort and console those who now walk in sorrow. We thank Him for each life we now must mourn, and the promise of a life to come.

13. As we have been assured, neither death nor life, nor angels nor principalities nor powers, nor things present nor things to come, nor height nor depth, can separate us from God's love. May He bless the souls of the departed. May He comfort our own. And may He always guide our country.

14. God bless America.

Sample Student Speech To Entertain

T.V. Times
by Amy Jo Hibinger

Specific Purpose: To entertain my audience with tales of the presence of television in our culture.

Central Idea: By using statistics and people's behaviors we can see television's power in our culture and can be warned to make sure we stay in control of our lives.

Pattern of Organization: Topical

In the two score and ten years since its entry into American homes, television has become the American pastime. Show me please, how many of you have access to T.V. where you live on campus? How many of you have watched T.V. today? How many of you watched it while you should have been working on your speeches? I'm majoring in broadcast journalism, so I have the advantage of being able to claim I am doing homework when I spend time in front of the tube. Through my course work, I have learned whether we examine **television through the lens of statistics or through our cultural behaviors**, we must admit television plays a central role in the life of our nation. **[metaphor]**

The *Wilson Quarterly* reports 99 percent of American homes have televisions. A 1995 survey by Fairbanks, Maslin & Associates revealed 66 percent of U.S. households have three or more sets. "So what?" you may counter, "probably 99 percent of American homes have a toilet, and it's likely that nearly half have two or more "thrones," but that doesn't mean we haven't got anything better to do than to sit on them all the time." Well, let's not be hasty in presuming all people put as high a priority on bathroom comforts as they do on television; as *Harper's Magazine* reports, in China the ratio of people who own television sets to those who have hot running water is 84 to 1.

Not only do we have televisions in our homes but also we use them. The Nielsen Company itself reports that the average American watches more than four hours of TV each day. The supporters of National TV-Turnoff Week have put that figure into perspective for us. Four hours a day means 28 hours a week, or two months of non-stop TV watching a year. By age 65, the members of the first television generation will have spent the equivalent of 9 years watching TV! Now mind you, this four hours a day estimate is conservative and refers only to actual viewing time. Televisions are turned on in American homes an average of nearly 7 and three quarter hours a day.

That three and three quarter hour difference between the average number of hours the T.V. is on and the average number of hours people actually view it suggests our television behaviors are quite odd. Karl Marx once labeled religion "the opiate of the masses." Some **contemporary cultural critics cry** that television now serves that role.**[alliteration]** Television has certainly advanced to a central place in our lives. Just walk into any home, and **there it is, sitting like an idol [simile]**. We elevate it on top of special furniture; seats are arranged to give everyone the best possible view; lighting is fixed to prevent glare. Members of households gather to worship. **Alone, they come; in family**

groups, they come; with friends, they come [parallelism]. Some enter the **sacred space** on a regular **schedule; some stop** before it to meditate in its presence at every possible moment **[alliteration].**

The idol is not a passive force, but rather, a force of great power [metaphor]. When **pilgrims** are drawn into its presence, **the outer world fades while the inner world dances with lights, color and warmth [metaphor].** It's happened to all of us; mom, a friend, even a boss who happens to call when I'm in the middle of the "CSI" just can't get my attention away from the tube. Even when I don't particularly care for what I'm watching, I can't seem to give a caller my undivided attention when the T.V. is on. I've switched long distance services and ordered useless magazines while in a television-induced stupor.

We all have confessions to make, don't we? How many of you actively avoid evening commitments on at least one night a week so you can see your favorite show? How many of you have spent the last few dollars of your meager checking accounts on your cable bill while leaving a textbook for a class unpurchased due to insufficient funds? How many of you have cried when your TIVO failed to capture what you wanted? How many of you arrange your class schedule so that you are free to indulge in an afternoon soap opera? I used to be addicted to soaps, but when I started losing sleep **worrying about the social lives of non-existent people (rather than worrying about my own non-existent social life),** I had to give it up. **[antithesis]** My name is Amy Jo, and I am a recovering soap-aholic.

We laugh, and yet Rutgers University psychologist Robert Kubey argues that heavy T.V. viewers exhibit six dependency symptoms—any four of which psychologists would consider evidence of substance abuse: "(1) using T.V. as a sedative; (2) indiscriminate use (viewing); (3) feeling loss of control while viewing; (4) feeling angry with oneself for watching too much; (5) inability to stop watching; and (6) feeling miserable when kept from watching."

The statistics are staggering: we spend one sixth of the day—nearly a third of our waking hours—glued to the tube. We have a culture where **television holds center stage [metaphor].** Some of us may even exhibit symptoms of substance abuse in our television viewing behaviors. How do you use the tube? Is your habit better or worse than the national average? Do you want to continue to see 20,000 thirty-second advertisements a year? Perhaps televisions should carry warning labels just like cigarettes: "Stopping viewing now will add years to your productive life." I guess we better get used to cutting back, after all, when we land those great jobs after college, the boss probably won't let us have time off in the afternoon to catch our soaps.

Bibliography
"Children Now." National poll, January 16-19, 1995, by Fairbanks, Maslin & Associates.
Gomery, Douglas. "As the Dial Turns." *Wilson Quarterly*. Autumn 1993, p. 42.
"Harper's Index." *Harper's Magazine*. March 1995, p. 12.
TV Facts and Figures. 20 October 2004. TV-Turnoff Network. 06 June 2005
<http://www.tvturnoff.org/>.

Sample Student Speech To Entertain

Beards

By Eric Sims Brown

Specific Purpose: To entertain my audience by celebrating the facial hair known as the Beard.

Central Idea: Growing a beard has helped me refine my self-identity by gaining me respect, attention and new-found patience.

Pattern of Organization: Topical

Growing up I was always something. Always the **shortest** or the **smallest, slowest** or the **shiest. [alliteration].** Physically I was not then and am not now the most impressive human being. This all changed for me recently. I've decided to make a lifestyle change. What change you might ask? Did I start exercising, eating right? Did I start wearing deodorant, maybe wear matching clothes? No, it's not what I started doing, it's what I stopped doing. I put down my razor; I put down my shaving cream and decided to give thanks for the wonder that is facial hair.

And you'd be surprised by the results. A **well-groomed face pet** demands respect. **[metaphor]** I remember an encounter I had about ten years ago. I was in line at the local grocery store. The checker, a middle-aged woman with a smoker's yellow skin, smiled at me, coffee stains on her teeth. I was nineteen at the time; pale with residual teenage acne and most importantly – no facial hair. The checker stared with a look of muddled recognition. She never took her eyes off me even as she scanned **the eggs – beep, the milk – beep, the bread – beep. [parallelism]** She paused as she placed the bread inside the bag, leaned into me and said with her gravelly voice, "I know you; you're on my son's middle school basketball team, right?" I lied and told her I played center – but that's beside the point. Such happenings do not occur when you've got a lush thicket of hair sprouting from chin and cheeks. You look older – more mature and if you're wearing a red plaid shirt you even look a little like the Brawny man. And no one would think the Brawny man plays middle school boys basketball.

And that's not all. A **well-worn face sweater** demands attention. **[metaphor]** A hairless face is like a **Christmas tree without the lights or ornaments. [simile]** On any given day the same person can look refined, grizzly, tough, gentle, psychotic, intelligent, cuddly or possibly even creepy. Think about the people you know with beards. Perhaps a grandfather, father, friend. Need another example? Picture Abe Lincoln in your mind. What do you see? A top hat, mole – beard. Would it seem strange to see these people fur free? I know some of you might be thinking "sure it'd be strange at first but we'd get used to the change." You might be right, but with that logic a person could essentially tape a pickle to their face and achieve the same results. Still, the shift would be noteworthy. A beard or any other form of facial hair seems to become part of a person's identity – part their personality.

And finally **a carefully manicured face forest** demands patience.**[metaphor]** At first there might be patches; picture an incomplete Panama Canal that doesn't necessarily connect one side to the other. However, given enough time, things should fill in nicely. The hair might be itchy—like wool socks are sprouting out your pores. Again, this will pass, I'd say give it two to three weeks. In the meantime you can perfect the beard stroke. You've probably seen it before.   It's that faraway gaze coupled with the **soft pet** between thumb and pointer finger. **[metaphor]** It's a look that signals "yes, I am thinking about seagulls, isn't that mysterious" or "I'd love to be curled up by a fire reading some poetry." Now, your significant other may not love the newest addition to the relationship. The whiskers are prickly and for a while you do give off the air of someone who plays video games until five in the morning. You're greasy and unkempt. In my experience he or she will come to accept the beard. I know my girlfriend certainly dreads the day when I may decide to shave off Leopold and return to my pre-pubescent state – or as I call it – my Macaulay Culkin days.

Beards, they're beautiful, buxom, bodacious and let's face it, they're kinda bad.[alliteration] They have the power to change our appearance, to make us appear older, perhaps more refined. A beard becomes part of who we are, but the decision to grow one shouldn't be entered into lightly. **A beard is a baby, it requires time and a lot of energy. [metaphor]** Those of us without one needn't feel bad. Everyone has something that sets them apart, maybe you have a distinctive voice or eye color, maybe you have a unique laugh or interesting arms. This is you, or at least part of you. **Because after all we are not defined by our traits, we define our traits. In the same way a beard doesn't make the person, the person makes the beard. [antithesis]**

Stylistic Devices Exercise

Using creative language is one of the challenging requirements of this assignment. In order to help you avoid tired old clichés such as "caught like a deer in the head lights," "solid as a rock," or "stank like garbage," or confusing similes (such as my personal favorite from a speech about John Lennon: "Like 'a ship lost out on the ocean,' John felt emptiness and bitterness."), and to inspire your creativity, I've taken some excerpts from both student speeches and famous speeches. As you read them, identify the stylistic devices used (there is often more than one) and think about how you might use similar devices to get more creative as you construct your own special occasion speech.

1. "There was still a blanket of snow covering the ground and everyone's breath still held visibly in the air like smoke."

Device(s) used: ___metaphor + similie___

2. "Just like an iceberg, the most important dimensions of culture are below the surface."

Device(s) used: ___simile___ .

3. "They ask: 'Is it worth losing valuable sleep and rest time on the weekend to get up so early just to fish?' These people have never quietly slipped in a slough as the sun rises. These people have never been on a river before anyone else when the only sounds to be heard are the silvery splashes of fish breaking the silk-like surface of the lake. These people have never spent a day in silent communion with the spirit of the lake."

Device(s) used: ___repetition + parallelism?___

4. "And though he left this world without ever making the pages of a history book, he still left the world an important life story—and in the pages of his life, in his everyday acts, I find his spirit—a spirit of unconditional, selfless, and inspiring love."

Device(s) used: ___antithesis + metaphor___

5. "Because most towns in Iowa are fairly small, everybody knows everybody, so gossip spreads like a disease. And there's no cure for it either. You can't take antibiotics or drugs to make it go away, in fact, despite what logic would tell you, any attempt to make it go away will just make it worse."

Device(s) used: ___metaphor___

6. "I was a ninja, ready to strike with precision, grace, and hopefully, accuracy"

Device(s) used: ___metaphor___

7. "My cheeks painted red, I felt the weight of defeat and shame make a home in my gut, but I wasn't about to give up."

Device(s) used: ___personification, metaphor, imagery___

105

8. Excerpts from John F. Kennedy's Inaugural Address Jan. 20, 1961

"Let every nation know, whether it wishes us well or ill, that we shall pay any price, bear any burden, meet any hardship, support any friend, oppose any foe to assure the survival and the success of liberty."

Device(s) used: _parallelism/repetition , maybe some alliteration_

"We dare not tempt them with weakness. For only when our arms are sufficient beyond doubt can we be certain beyond doubt that they will never be employed."

Device(s) used: _~~to~~ parallelism_ .

9. From Ronald Reagan's Inaugural Address, January 20, 1981:

"I do not believe in a fate that will fall on us no matter what we do. I do believe in a fate that will fall on us if we do nothing. So with all the creative energy at our command, let us begin an era of national renewal. Let us renew our determination, our courage, and our strength."

Device(s) used: _parallelism, repetition , antithesis_

10. Booker T. Washington, Atlanta Exposition Address, September 18, 1895:
This speech remains controversial in part because of the following line which seemed to uphold the segregation policies so rampant at the time.

"In all things that are purely social we can be as separate as the fingers, yet one as the hand in all things essential to mutual progress."

Device(s) used: _metaphor_

11. Angelina Grimké in her famous anti-slavery speech of 1838 given in Pennsylvania Hall. *There is a large mob of anti-abolitionist protesters outside the hall–they protest the agitation of the slavery question and protest women speaking in public. Grimké addresses an audience fearful of the mob outside. Their fears are legitimate for that very night the mob returns and burns down the hall.*

"Animated with hope, nay with an assurance of the triumph of liberty and good will to man, I will lift up my voice like a trumpet, and show this people their transgression."

Device(s) used: _simile , personification_

"There is nothing to be feared from those who would stop our mouths, but they themselves should fear and tremble. The current is even now setting fast against them. If the arm of the North had not caused the Bastille of slavery to totter to its foundation, you would not hear those cries."

Device(s) used: _metaphor, personification_

12. Clinton's First Inaugural Address, January 1993

"And I thank the millions of men and women whose steadfastness and sacrifice triumphed over depression, fascism, and communism. Today, a generation raised in the shadow of the cold war assumes new responsibilities in a world warmed by the sunshine of freedom but threatened still by ancient hatreds and new plagues."

Device(s) used: _metaphors, personification_

13. Alice Walker, "What Can the White Man Say to the Black Woman" April 8, 1989:

"I will free your children from insultingly high infant mortality rates, short life spans, horrible housing, lack of food, rampant ill health. I will liberate them from the ghetto. I will open wide the doors of all the schools and hospitals and businesses of society to your children. I will look at your children and see not a threat but a joy."

Device(s) used: _parallelism, repetition_

14. George W. Bush: Address to a Joint Session of Congress on Terrorist Attacks, September 20, 2001

"Some speak of an age of terror. I know there are struggles ahead, and dangers to face. But this country will define our times, not be defined by them."

Device(s) used: _antithesis_

15. Arnold Schwarzenegger: 2004 Republican National Convention Address; August 31, 2004

"I finally arrived here in 1968. What a special day it was. I remember I arrived here with empty pockets, but full of dreams, full of determination, full of desire."

Device(s) used: _repetition & alliteration_

16. Barack Obama: 2004 Democratic National Convention Address, July 27, 2004

"And he knows that it's not enough for just some of us to prosper—for alongside our famous individualism, there's another ingredient in the American saga, a belief that we're all connected as one people. If there is a child on the south side of Chicago who can't read, that matters to me, even if it's not my child. If there is a senior citizen somewhere who can't pay for their prescription drugs, having to choose between medicine and the rent, that makes my life poorer, even if it's not my grandparent. If there's an Arab American family being rounded up without benefit of an attorney or due process that threatens my civil liberties."

Device(s) used: _parallelism_

Tips for Delivering a Speech from a Manuscript

When writing the speech:

1. *Write for the ear.*

    Read your writing out loud as you create and edit the speech. Not only will this increase your familiarity with the text, but it will help you to achieve the style of elevated conversation. It will also help you to attend to the rhythm of your language.

2. *Use stylistic devices to help reinforce structure and the memorability of your words.*

    Devices such as parallelism, repetition, and alliteration will help you to structure your work and will make it easier for you to recall passages during delivery.

When delivering the speech:

1. *Create a manuscript that will assist you.*

    A delivery manuscript will have enormous margins, generous spacing, and a large font size. In addition, it will contain highlighting and delivery cues that will remind you to look at the audience, pause, smile, or breathe.

2. *Look at the audience while you speak.*

    Rather than looking down continuously and reading from the manuscript, aim to look down only briefly to "photograph" a chunk of the text and then look up to deliver it. Work to make eye contact with as many individuals in the room as you can.

3. *Use vocal delivery skills to assist you.*

    Beware of falling into a monotone "reading voice." Use pauses and vocal variety (changes in pitch, rate, and inflection) to draw attention to your ideas and to your special use of language. Be sure to give audiences enough time to feel the impact of your words.

4. *Practice with the manuscript.*

    Rehearse the speech with the same text repeatedly so that you know exactly where to look when you glance down for a passage. Try to simulate your actual speaking environment as much as possible—create a podium out of books or rehearse in the speaking room.

5. *Don't worry about getting the words exactly as you wrote them.*

    While the point of manuscript delivery is to exercise greater care than usual in delivering a particular text, do not be afraid to let the moment inspire you. Feel free to add or delete a word or elaborate on a point to adapt to feedback. The speech event remains a dynamic atmosphere and you need to be open to moments of inspiration. In 1963 on the steps of the Lincoln Memorial, Martin Luther King, Jr. went off of his manuscript to include a passage he had used parts of in some earlier speeches. He felt an inspiration in that moment and now the speech is best known for his unplanned, unscripted "I Have a Dream" sequence. Most important is the need to resist the temptation to start the whole paragraph over when you lose your place. Instead, try to make it make sense with a temporary detour and then come back to your text.

Special Occasion Speech Manuscript Checklist

These are the criteria your instructor will use to grade your manuscript.

Specific Purpose Statement [1 pt.]
   • stated at the top of the outline
   • follows the chapter 4 guidelines for Specific Purpose Statements	

Central Idea Statement [1 pt.]
   • stated at the top of the outline
   • follows the chapter 4 guidelines for stating Central Ideas	

Pattern of Organization [1 pt.]
   • stated at the top of the outline
   • pattern of organization is correctly identified	

Manuscript Structure [2 pts.]
   • text has a clear Introduction, Body, Conclusion
   • if the speech uses source material, there is a solid bibliography	

Stylistic Devices [5 pts.]
   • at least 5 **labeled and bolded** stylistic devices in the manuscript
   • examples of at least **three** different types of devices are employed
   • labels for devices are accurate	

Miscellaneous Materials

Special Occasion Speech to Entertain Feedback Form

Speaker _____

Topic _____

Rate the speaker on each point:	O-outstanding		S-satisfactory	N–needs work
Introduction gained attention	O	S	N	
Subject introduced clearly	O	S	N	
Main ideas easily followed	O	S	N	
Conclusion reinforced the central idea	O	S	N	
Topic dealt with creatively	O	S	N	
Stylistic devices included	O	S	N	
Stylistic devices used effectively	O	S	N	
Supporting materials entertaining	O	S	N	
Humor appropriate	O	S	N	
Originality of thought and expression	O	S	N	
Sufficient eye contact	O	S	N	
Voice used effectively	O	S	N	
Nonverbal communication effective	O	S	N	
Presentation of self strong	O	S	N	
Speech adapted to audience	O	S	N	
Speech had intended impact on audience	O	S	N	

Comments

Speech Recording Reflection Assignment

Record your speech following your lab instructor's instructions. Follow the process below in order to listen to and reflect on the recording of your speech. Record your responses <u>on another sheet of paper </u>and turn it in to your lab instructor by the date assigned. Be sure to include your name, the specific purpose of your speech and your instructor's name at the top of the page.

1. Listen to your speech all the way through concentrating on the content of your message. Did you accomplish your specific purpose? Why or why not? Were the main points clear? Did you hear support material and proper citations?

2. Turn down the volume and watch the speech again focusing only on your physical delivery. Did your body help to maintain audience attention and interest? What did you do with your hands? With your feet? Do your facial expressions seem consistent with what you were talking about? Where do you seem to be looking most of the time during the speech? If you used visual aids in your speech, what did you notice about your delivery when using them?

3. Turn up the volume and turn down the brightness or look away from your screen so that you can just listen to the speech. Does your voice help to carry the message to the audience? Does it <u>sound</u> informative/persuasive? Does the rate and the pitch vary in a way that both fits with the content and meets the audience's need for variety? Does verbal delivery help make the message clear and powerful? Are there any filled pauses, mispronounced words, or startling grammar problems?

4. Having watched your speech at least three times, what would you say were three of its major strengths?

5. What would you say were two of its major weaknesses?

6. What would you like to do differently the next time you speak?

Impromptu Speech Assignment

Description

The impromptu speech is the classic "off-the-cuff" exercise. Impromptu speaking is very common in our culture; there will be occasions where you suddenly find yourself on the spot either responding to a question or feeling a compulsion to speak your mind about a subject under discussion. Our goal is to let you see how useful the tools that you have already learned in this course can be even when facing an unexpected speaking situation. Your lab instructor will talk to you about the specific details of your assignment. Chapter 12 in the textbook has some advice for delivering impromptu speeches.

Preparation

There is little you can do to prepare for this speech. Still, as you think about the exercise, as you work on it in your preparation time, and as you face impromptu speaking challenges in the future, you must certainly consider issues of creativity and structure. Once you know your topic, think of a point (central idea) you want to make about it. Next imagine two or three main things you want to say (like main points). As you begin to speak make sure that the topic is clear to the listeners and that you preview your main ideas. Using signposts is a great idea when doing impromptu speaking since it helps not only the audience, but also you to keep track of your ideas. Finally, make sure you bring the speech to a conclusion with a nice closing line.

Requirements

In this course, successful impromptu speakers will do the following:

1. Speak within the time limit.

2. Develop the topic clearly (stick to the point).

3. Have a sense of structure

4. Look at the audience while speaking

5. Have an identifiable conclusion

6. Have reasonably poised delivery.

A Decade in Pursuit of Kony

Outside Speech Observation Form
This Form Must Be Submitted Within 1 week of the Speech
Submitting via Blackboard is preferred

Your Name: Rhonda Berry

Lab Section # 3   Lab Instructor's Name: Justin Atwell

PART I--General Information:

Date Speech was attended:

April 9, 2012

Where was it delivered?

Sun Room in the Memorial Union

Name and Title/Role of the Speaker:

Bobby Bailey, co-founder of "Invisible Children" and an anti-poverty organization

Approximate number of people in the audience:

≈50 -75

Create a Specific Purpose Statement for the presentation:

in general

To inspire the audience to change the world, & to continue the work to stop the atrocities in Uganda (specifically)

PART II--Discussion of the Speech

1. In the Introduction steps did the speaker take to:

a. gain attention?

began with humor, joking about his outfit

b. establish his or her credibility?

described his personal experience/journey that led him to a life of advocacy for children in Uganda
summary of career in harsh language

2. List 2 ways the speaker attempted to relate to the audience or to keep their attention? How effective were their efforts to engage the audience?

-Use of clear, plain, harsh, & emotional language

-Conversational style, surprising & eye-popping examples, personal note
multimedia

139

3. List the main points of the speech

1. How I (he) found himself in Africa
2. Situation in Africa — warlords, manipulators, displaced & abducted kids, etc.
3. Making of / Story behind "Invisible Children" movie/organization
   — model for making change in the world
   "Alive" acronym

who is going to rise as the next leader?

Accept no boundaries
Learn
If broken, invent new models
Voice
Expand

4. <u>Describe</u> the speaker's delivery skills for each of the following categories:
a. eye contact: almost always on the audience, roving over all the listeners

b. gestures: resting position of hands at chest height, but they were almost constantly in motion, emphasizing points

c. vocal variety: lots of changes in volume, lots of tone & emotion variety

d. posture/stance: comfortable, moving and stepping, leaning forward to emphasize points

5. In the Conclusion what steps did the speaker take to:
a. Signal the end of the speech
   Mentioned the present void in leadership, challenged us to rise as leaders

b. Reinforce the Central idea

6. Which term best describes the audience response to the speaker? (circle one)

1. bored   2. polite   3. appreciative   4. enthusiastic

7. Why do you think the audience responded this way?

He had good media & good style, but I didn't feel really called to action, & it was late. I think these affects were on everyone

140

Outside Speech Observation Form <u>Bonus</u>
<u>This Form Must Be Submitted Within 1 week of the Speech</u>
<u>Submitting via Blackboard is preferred</u>

Your Name:_____

Lab Section #_____ Lab Instructor's Name:_____

PART I--General Information:

Date Speech was attended:

Where was it delivered?

Name and Title/Role of the Speaker:

Approximate number of people in the audience:

Create a Specific Purpose Statement for the presentation:

PART II--Discussion of the Speech

1. In the Introduction steps did the speaker take to:

   a. gain attention?

   b. establish his or her credibility?

2. List 2 ways the speaker attempted to relate to the audience or to keep their attention? How effective were their efforts to engage the audience?

3. List the main points of the speech

4. <u>Describe</u> the speaker's delivery skills for each of the following categories:
   a. eye contact:

   b. gestures:

   c. vocal variety:

   d. posture/stance:

5. In the Conclusion what steps did the speaker take to:
   a. Signal the end of the speech

   b. Reinforce the Central idea

6. Which term best describes the audience response to the speaker? (circle one)

1. bored   2. polite   3. appreciative   4. enthusiastic

7. Why do you think the audience responded this way?

"I Gave a Speech!" An Exercise in Learning by Reflection

Your assignment is to help yourself become a better speaker through practice and reflection outside the SpCm 212, or any other, classroom. For purposes of this bonus assignment the speech should be a prepared address of at least 10 minutes in length* delivered to an audience this semester outside of any course taken for academic credit. ***Your reflection should be approximately 1.5 pp. single spaced and is due within 1 week of the delivery of your presentation.***

Begin this exercise by reviewing the parts of the Roman Rhetorical canon that we have covered this semester:

> ***inventio*** [invention]: analyzing their audience, finding materials, creating ideas for the speech, creating/designing a visual aid
>
> ***dispositio*** [arrangement]:: helping them arrange their speech, create a good introduction and conclusion and to develop an easy to follow outline
>
> ***elocutio*** [language/style]: helping to edit and enliven the verbal expression of the speech–to guide word choice (make sure it isn't too technical or too dull) and to encourage some use of stylistic devices to add attention, interest, and impact to the speech.
>
> ***pronunciatio*** [delivery]: coaching them in aspects of verbal and non-verbal delivery
>
> ***memoria*** [memory]: strategies for recalling the material of the speech

Choose one or two of the above issues as a focal point for your written reflection. You might choose those that were most problematic for you or were most complex or simply that concept you find most interesting. Type up your responses to all 6 questions, save the file and submit by uploading it to Blackboard (or following your Lab Instructors instructions). For questions 4- 6 below you should respond in depth and answer the questions with particular attention to the concept(s) identified in question 3.

---

1. Context. What was the occasion/situation for the speech? [Identify the date, time, place, type of situation and size and composition of the audience. *Be sure to complete this assignment within a week*.]

2. Describe. What was the goal (specific purpose) of the speech you gave? Who determined the goal (you or the person asking you to speak?) How long was the speech and who determined the length?

3. Which of the four parts of the Roman Rhetorical Canon will focus on in your reflection?

4. What were the specific challenges you faced relative to the concept noted in question 3? Be specific and detailed in your response.

5. What were the choices you made concerning that rhetorical canon? Be specific and detailed.

6. Do you believe that you were effective in implementing that rhetorical canon? Why or why not? Be specific and detailed in your response. Feel free to refer not only to your own perceptions, but also to feedback you may have received during and after the presentation.

*Being part of a group presentation can qualify you, but your part of the presentation must have been at least 10 minutes.

The Finishing Touch:
Tips for Facilitating Question and Answer Sessions

A strong question and answer session is often a key part of a successful oral presentation. It offers a great opportunity for you to interact with the audience and to gain immediate feedback about the ideas raised in your talk, so it is essential that you are prepared to respond to questions and to competently facilitate the session.

To Prepare for Q & A

Anticipate
Find out how speakers typically handle Q & A sessions within this speaking environment. Will listeners expect to be able to interrupt you to ask their questions or will they follow the traditional structure of holding questions until the end?
Consider the likely questions and formulate possible responses before your presentation.

Practice
Articulate responses to likely questions. This is especially important if your presentation is likely to provoke controversy. You need to plan your strategies to clarify or further support your positions in a respectful manner.
Rehearse sharing extra examples or stories that can bolster your case.

Adapt
Be flexible in your presentation so that you can accommodate the Q & A session. If your listeners expect a highly interactive session, be sure to reduce the length of your speech as needed to allow for the exchange.

Prepare
Create a clear closing line for the Q & A session. Work on a gracious way to indicate the end of the question and answer session and to leave the audience with a positive impression.

To Facilitate Q & A

Clarify Intention
Establish a sense of how much time there is for the question and answer session. (Either you or the person running the session should say something such as: "It looks like we have 15 minutes left for questions" or "I'll be happy to take 3 or 4 questions before we adjourn.") Be firm about cutting off questions when the predetermined limit is up.

Listen Carefully and Restate
This helps you clarify the question, ensures that the entire audience hears the question, and gives you a moment to consider your response.

Speak to the Group
Direct your response to the entire audience rather than only to the questioner.

Be Brief
Give simple answers to simple questions. When faced with a complicated or unwieldy question, answer concisely and then offer to meet the questioner later for further discussion.

Be Straightforward
If you do not know the answer to a particular question, refer the question to someone else or offer to get back to the questioner with an answer.

Prime the Pump
If an audience seems hesitant to ask questions, yet there is plenty of time left, consider asking a question of the audience. Or share an interesting question someone else asked you recently and respond to it.

Maintain Control
Do not allow one person to dominate the question and answer session or turn the session into a debate. Try to maintain momentum to sustain the interest of your audience. If a questioner is hostile, avoid responding defensively and aim to stay calm. Try restating/reshaping the question or just try reflective listening: "so you are saying _____; I have not really been thinking along those lines." This strategy validates the questioner without undermining your credibility. Signaling a willingness to continue the conversation at a later time is generally regarded as a mark of an ethical speaker.

Close Confidently
Use your prepared closing or something developed in the moment so that your presentation ends on a confident, professional note.

Informative Speech Topic Form

Name: _____   **Lab Instructor:** _____

Identify two topics you would be comfortable developing for your Informative Speech. Then answer the following questions about your preferred topic idea below. Use the back of the page as needed.

1(a). What is the Specific Purpose of your preferred topic? Aim to use proper form, as in: "To inform my audience how GPS systems increase crop yields."

1(b) What is the Specific Purpose of your alternative topic?

2. Your preferred topic idea is an example of which of the types of speeches described by the Informative Speech Assignment page in the workbook?   <u>Underline</u> one of these options:

Option A [my major]   B [interesting course concept]   C [communication concept]

3. What special ideas or experiences do you bring to your preferred topic?

4. How will you connect your preferred topic to your audience?

5. What visual aids might help you to share your preferred topic with your audience? Why?

6. What pattern of organization might best fit your preferred topic? Why? (refer to ch. 8)

7. What questions do you have about how best to succeed with your preferred topic?

Persuasive Speech Topic Ideas Analysis

Name _____ Lab Instructor _____

1(a). What is the Specific Purpose of your *preferred* topic and what personal credibility do you bring to this topic?
[Use proper form as in: To persuade my audience to donate blood during the Red Cross Blood Drive. OR To persuade my audience that the state of Iowa should outlaw all use of cell phones while driving.]

(b) What is the Specific Purpose of your alternative topic and what personal credibility do you bring to this topic?

2. What pattern of organization might best fit your each of these topics? Why? (Consult the textbook discussion in chapter 15 for patterns of organization for persuasive speeches.)

-Choose one of the topics you have listed to answer the remaining questions-

3. Who is the "we" in the Specific Purpose of your preferred topic? (Who is going to carry out the action you are trying to persuade us about? If you cannot really answer this question for your preferred topic, then you need to revise your topic.)

4. What are the **problems** that you propose to solve? What is wrong with the status quo (the way things are)? (For this and the following question, consult the discussion of the Problem (Need), Plan, and Practicality issues in chapter 15 of the textbook. Note: if you can't answer these questions easily, you need to reconsider your topic.)

5. What is the precise **plan** you propose should be adopted? Who will be acting? What do you want your listeners to do? Be specific.

6. What are at least 2 objections your listeners are likely to have in regards to the problem you are addressing or about the plan you are proposing, and how do you plan to overcome these objections? (For example, it is unlikely that people in your audience would object to ISU lowering the cost of tuition so a speech advocating this action could be a weak topic. If very few people would object to your topic then you need to reconsider the topic or at least make sure that you are prepared to rise to the real challenge of the speech that requires you to MOTIVATE the audience to do something or believe that change is necessary.)

7. Identify 2 or more questions that you have about how best to succeed with this topic that you can bring up during workshop.

Researching the Persuasive Speech: Worksheet

Name: _____ TA and Section #: _____

This assignment is designed to accomplish two tasks:
- to help you find good research materials for your own persuasive speech topic.
- to make you familiar with the wide range of quality research materials available, even electronically, through ISU's library.

Step One: Identify topic terms for your search

Write down your topic term and at least two other terms related to it. For example, if your topic is recycling, write: "recycling," "landfills," and "e-waste" If your topic is the Americans with Disabilities Act, you can write that topic and terms such as "disabilities, legal," "building codes," and "Universal Design."

1. _____ 2. _____

3. _____ 4._____

Step Two: Gather Materials

Go On-line to: http://instr.iastate.libguides.com/spcm212 [You can also get there through the link on your 212 Blackboard Homepage.]   Click through the tabs on the site for helpful information on "Beginning Research" and "Resources." There is also info here to help you evaluate the materials you find here and through other Internet searches as well as citation guides.

Under the "Resources" tab choose a resource to begin your research. The best choices are the links to "Academic Search Elite," "LexisNexis Academic," and the EBSCOHost Databases. A source like AcademicSearch Elite will give you access to over 60 million articles that have been reviewed by experts so they are more trustworthy and are less apt to be biased than other resources found on the Internet. From any campus computer, or by logging into the ISU Library Site with your PIN, you can access many of full text articles from these great sources.

Start exploring these resources by using the search terms above.

Step Three: Research, Read, Reflect, Record and submit on Blackboard

Find 5 relevant articles—journals, magazines, newspapers, editorial, proceedings, etc.—review them and record information about them below.

Here is an example: *In AcademicSearch Elite, I searched for "e-waste." I found an article called "How Much E-waste is there in US Basements and Attics?" After reading the abstract and reading the article briefly, I saved it to my flash drive. I then cut and pasted the citation onto this form and answered the other two questions on the form as follows:*

Bibliographic Information (Author (s), Article Title, Where & When it was Published)

Saphores, Jean-Daniel M.; Nixon, Hilary; Ogunseitan, Oladele A.; Shapiro, Andrew A. "How much e-waste is there in US basements and attics? Results from a national survey." Journal of Environmental Management, Aug 2009, Vol. 90 Issue 11, p3322-3331.

Brief Summary of Article: This research team argues that creating a strong recycling infrastructure for e-waste is important, but that motivating people to do so is hard because there isn't good data about how much e-waste people are accumulating in their homes. Their survey of 2136 US households helped them create this report indicating that the amount of e-waste in our homes is much higher than old estimates suggest. They claim that "on average, each US household has 4.1 small (≤10 pounds) and 2.4 large e-waste items in storage."

State how you might find this resource useful: This article will help me establish the Problem section of my speech because it proves that the amount of e-waste already in people's homes is significant.

Resource 1
Bibliographic Information (Author, Article Title, Where & When it was Published)

Brief Summary of Article:

State how you might find this resource useful:

Resource 2
Bibliographic Information (Author, Article Title, Where & When it was Published)

Brief Summary of Article:

State how you might find this resource useful:

Resource 3
Bibliographic Information (Author, Article Title, Where & When it was Published)

Brief Summary of Article:

State how you might find this resource useful:

Resource 4
Bibliographic Information (Author, Article Title, Where & When it was Published)

Brief Summary of Article:

State how you might find this resource useful:

Resource 5
Bibliographic Information (Author, Article Title, Where & When it was Published)

Brief Summary of Article:

State how you might find this resource useful:

Special Occasion Speech Topic Form

Name: _____   Lab Instructor: _____

Identify two topics you would be comfortable developing for your Special Occasion Speech. Then answer the following questions about your preferred topic ideas below. Use the back of the page as needed.

1. What is the General Purpose (i.e., to inspire or to entertain) and the Specific Purpose of your preferred topic?

2. What is the General Purpose (i.e., to inspire or to entertain) and the Specific Purpose of your alternative topic?

3. What is the central idea for the speech? (aim to create a CI that captures all of the main points of your speech)

4. What pattern of organization do you expect to use for your preferred topic? Why?

5. If the General Purpose of your preferred topic is commemorative or "to inspire," list the values on which you will focus; if it is an after-dinner or speech "to entertain," elaborate on the support materials you will select from for their entertainment value.

Here's an example:
1. General Purpose: Commemorative--to inspire; Specific Purpose: To inspire my audience by telling them about the values I learned from my grandfather.
3. Central Idea: My grandfather lived a life of compassion, tolerance, and courage.
4. Pattern of Organization: Topical. The speech will be based on three values my grandfather taught me. It will tell stories from his life, but each of the values will be one main point, so that is topical.
5. In this speech I will talk about my grandfather's compassion by giving examples of his kindness to others. I'll show how he taught me tolerance by living a life that accepted all types of people. Mostly I will focus on the courage he showed by saving a little girl's life and by fighting leukemia. I hope to inspire my audience by showing them what I learned from him. I will use parallel structure and concrete language to add to the impact of the speech.